FIREHOUSES

NICHOLAS J. HAYES
THOMAS W. CHURCHILL
WILLIAM A. DOYLE
EDWARD F. CROKER
ALFRED M. DOWNES
ALEXANDER STEVENS
GEORGE HILDEBRAND
44 ENGINE COMPANY 44
ENG 44
CAUTION
WHEN ALARM BELL SOUNDS
TANK FILLED TO CAPACITY
DO NOT OVERFILL
DIAL 911
TRUE
HERO
DIESEL O

FIREHOUSES

ROB LEICESTER WAGNER

MetroBooks

MetroBooks

An Imprint of Friedman/Fairfax Publishers

Library of Congress Cataloging-in-Publication Data

Wagner, Rob, 1954 -.
Fire stations / by Rob Leicester Wagner.
p.cm.
Includes bibliographical references and index.
ISBN 1-58663-049-0 (alk. paper)
1. Fire extinction—History. 2. Fire stations. 3. Vernacular
architecture. I. Title.

TH9117 .W34 2001
363.37—dc21

00-045234

Editor: Susan Lauzau
Art Director: Kevin Ullrich
Designer: Jonathan Gaines
Photography Editor: Jami Ruszkai
Production Manager: Rosy Ngo
Color separations by Bright Arts Graphics (S) Pte Ltd.
Printed in China by C&C Offset Printing Co. Ltd.

1 3 5 7 9 10 8 6 4 2

For bulk purchases and special sales, please contact:
Friedman/Fairfax Publishers
Attention: Sales Department
15 West 26th Street
New York, NY 10010
212/685-6610 FAX 212/685-3916

Visit our website:
www.metrobooks.com

Previous: Firehouses reflected the neighborhoods in which they stood. Originally centerpieces of the community, they gradually became more integrated with the surrounding environment. This red brick structure typifies the city of New York's efforts to make use of limited Manhattan real estate, but still provide a structure that stands slightly above nearby buildings, both in aesthetic quality and physical dimensions.

DEDICATION

For Deniece

ACKNOWLEDGMENTS

In gathering information for this book I relied on the expertise of many people. Special thanks to Dennis Keenan, fire director of the Trenton (New Jersey) Fire Department; Bill Delaplaine, assistant fire chief of the Presidio Fire Department in San Francisco, California; Chandler McCoy, architect and project manager for the Presidio Trust; Pat and Joseph Donlon of the Peabody (Massachusetts) Historical Society; Pat Saur and Petronella Ytsma of St. Paul, Minnesota; Edith Schoenberg of Tivoli, New York; Dace Taube, curator of the Regional History Center, University of Southern California; Harvey B. Mack, curator of the Forest Service History Center of Corona, California; Jill Schofield, librarian at the Sierra Madre (California) Public Library; Ron Matthews, president of the board of directors of the Volunteer Firemen's Hall and Museum of Kingston, New York; and Harry Magee, firefighter for the Philadelphia Fire Department. Thanks also go to my editor, Susan Lauzau.

C O N T E N T S

HUTCHINSON
2
FIRE DEPT.
2
EPT.

Previous: In this early cab-over-engine ladder and hose truck belonging to the Hutchinson Fire Department, the driver and engineer ride in an unprotected cab. For decades, firefighters were expected to brave the elements to reach fires. It wasn't until after World War II that enclosed cabs became commonplace.

Right: The author's childhood inspiration: the thick adobe walls and tiled roof of this structure housed both city hall and the firehouse for the community of Sierra Madre, California. The arched windows and quatrefoil window above the entrance are remnants of the Mission style; the rest is classic Spanish Colonial.

INTRODUCTION

Dead center on the main drag of my hometown of Sierra Madre, California, stands the old city hall and firehouse. It has held up well over its seventy-three-year existence, thanks to a restoration project some years ago that transformed it into an office building.

The old city hall has become the town's icon, and today serves as a reminder of Southern California's frenzied period of Spanish Colonial Revival architecture in the 1920s. Standing on a corner lot at 55 West Sierra Madre Boulevard, the structure is classic Spanish Colonial, an extension of the earlier Mission style, which in turn was derived from Mediterranean influences. It suits this foothill city of nearly 11,000 people well.

By the mid 1960s, portions of the firehouse were no longer used. I recall that at one point it became something of a storage locker for odds and ends from city hall offices. But it always held center stage in town and in the community's heart. When I was a child, the town's volunteer fire department would hold its annual open house, giving everyone an opportunity to clamor over the Crown pumper and old Seagrave fire engines. But what was most intriguing to me as a young boy was the slide chute from the second-floor sleeping quarters to the garage. Even in those days (the early 1960s), it was dusty from years of disuse.

When constructing the city hall and the firehouse, the city leaders of the time knew precisely what they wanted. This central building was not to be an imposing structure of the kind found in larger cities. It was to be a structure that exuded authority but also represented the character of the town and the folks who lived in it. But that was just the beginning; the road to building the town's first firehouse was to be a long one.

Nestled at the base of the San Gabriel Mountains, Sierra Madre has always had to contend with brushfires.

CITY HALL
CAUTION
FIRE
STATION
SIERRA MADRE
ENG. NO. 1

Right: The care taken with the detail work on this Rodgers engine—built in 1851 for the Alexandria, Virginia, Friendship Fire Company—shows the esteem in which firefighters were held.

From its early days, there was considerable concern that a brushfire could whip through the canyon and threaten the village below. In the beginning, the town answered these concerns by ringing the Congregational Church bell whenever a fire was reported; at the sound of the bell every able-bodied man rushed to the scene with ax and bucket in hand.

This led to the formation of a volunteer fire department—not much more than a club for men—in 1909. The new fire department soon entered into a joint agreement with the city to build a firehouse. Although the city purchased a corner lot with every intention of building one, it took more than a decade to see it completed. Still, the volunteers muddled through, fighting the town's small fires and storing their engines at Milt Steinberger's garage down the street.

But their needs continued to grow. In 1919, the fire department was forced to seek help from the nearby Monrovia Fire Department to battle a particularly large fire. It was time for their own state-of-the-art, dedicated firehouse. Offered a parcel of land by the city, the volunteer fire department couldn't raise the necessary cash to build, and in 1921 the property was returned to the city. Finally, through a bond measure in the mid-1920s, the city raised $24,000, and plans for the firehouse could begin.

Local architect R.M. Finlayson was hired to design the facility. Southern Californians had long been enamored with the Mission and Spanish Colonial styles, and in designing the Sierra Madre City Hall and Firehouse, Finlayson remained true to the tradition. And he no doubt found inspiration in the works of California architect Irving Gill, perhap best known for his Mission-style buildings, which evoked the Spanish roots of California's early settlers. During the first decade of the twentieth century, some rather grandiose and eclectic variants of the traditional Mission-style theme had been produced in California, but Gill's designs returned to a simpler form that eschewed intricate details and celebrated the clean lines of traditional Spanish Colonial and Mission-style architecture.

Spanish Colonial Revival (also called Spanish Eclectic) is actually a compendium of styles that elaborated on the Spanish Mission and Colonial styles to include a wide variety of Spanish architectural motifs, including arched windows, plain wall surfaces, tiled roofs, and towers with pitched roofs. Gill's signature creamy stucco walls, red-tiled roofs, and wide, high arches can be seen in his Bishop's School in La Jolla, California (1909–16), the Women's Club of La Jolla (1913), and the Lewis Court residence of the same era in Sierra Madre.

Finlayson was probably also inspired by the Spanish Colonial style of Santa Barbara. After the 1925 earthquake created a need for extensive rebuilding in that city, there was a successful movement to accept Spanish Colonial as its official style. All the elements of Spanish Colonial Revival style, including exotic touches of Moorish and Gothic architecture in the quatrefoil window high above the front entrance, are found in Finlayson's city hall design.

Finlayson completed the Sierra Madre City Hall and Firehouse in late 1927 and hoped to have it occupied by New Year's Day, 1928. He missed his self-imposed deadline by three weeks. The *Sierra Madre News* announced that the building would be ready to be occupied on January 21. "Mañana, Spanish for tomorrow, is the password at the new City Hall," reported the *News*, "and it fits perfectly with the Spanish-type architecture, but not so perfectly with the plans of the city officials and the architect R. M. Finlayson, who had expected to have the building completed as a New Year's Day gift to the people of Sierra Madre."

While the delay might have disappointed Finlayson, the completed building soon became the heart of the city, and remained that way until both the city hall offices and the firehouse were moved to new quarters just down the street in 1976. Like the Sierra Madre firehouse, firehouses across the continent have been central figures in the communities where they stand, reflecting the nature of the place and its people in their design and architecture.

Today, the community firehouse has lost much of its character. The modern fire station is mainly a functional building that houses state-of-the-art equipment. And in many cases, if not most, it is among the least distinctive buildings in the city. Today's planners demand that the firehouse blend into a neighborhood, preferring that it be nearly identical in design to nearby residences or office buildings.

With the Sierra Madre City Hall and firehouse, the city's careful efforts to integrate a municipal building into the community and yet maintain its unique character were wildly successful. While Spanish Colonial fell out of favor as a style in the years immediately following World War II, it experienced a strong surge in popularity in the 1950s and today remains a timeless example of understated design. Yet it is a style seen almost exclusively in California and the Southwest. More universal throughout North America are the Romanesque and red-brick firehouses that gained popularity after the Civil War; Victorian and Edwardian designs of the late nineteenth and early twentieth centuries; and even the Prairie and Art Deco styles of later years. The architectural design adopted for the town firehouse often reflected the status of the firefighter in the community. In the late nineteenth century, when firefighters were regarded as nearly mythical heroes, opulent structures were built in their honor; that era witnessed the construction of firehouses in the grand style of European castles and palaces.

When motorized fire engines became commonplace in the 1920s, more practical designs were implemented and the castles and palaces were replaced by more functional and austere buildings. The era of extravagant firehouse architecture may be long past, but its history remains alive, as communities continue to invest in restoration projects to preserve their heritage.

Today, the exterior of the Sierra Madre building has been restored to it original splendor, although the tower is now gone due to earthquake safety concerns. The interior is split into three levels and is home to several small businesses, including quite fittingly, an architectural firm.

SHAW ISLAND FIRE DEPT.
ENGINE CO.
Nº 1

From Buckets to Tin Lizzies

As cities and towns sprang up in the New World, public safety was a concern that was little addressed, at least in the beginning. By the 1650s, towns filled with wood-frame structures were sprouting up everywhere, yet a strategy to battle large fires still seemed to be an afterthought. Town leaders may very well have been concerned about fire safety in the abstract, but they didn't appear to consider the ramifications of constructing wood-frame buildings with thatched roofs and wooden chimneys so close together.

Previous: The earliest firehouses were simple storage sheds for housing equipment, like this building belonging to the Shaw Island Fire Department, off the coast of Washington State.

Above: Although kept filled with water at all times, railroad fire buckets were generally ineffective in fighting anything but the smallest of fires.

But the dangers of this type of construction were very real. Sparks from a single chimney often resulted in conflagrations that consumed entire city blocks.

THE EARLY DAYS OF FIREFIGHTING

North America in the mid-seventeenth century was in dire need of equipment and a workable plan to combat fires. Still, obtaining functioning equipment to replace or at least complement human effort, finding a place to house that equipment, and creating a full contingent of firefighters on a twenty-four-hour watch would take two centuries to become a reality. It would take another century to perfect firefighting technology as it moved from bucket brigades and firefighting gangs to the steam and horse era, and finally to motorized fire engines. Along the way, over a three-hundred-year period, architects designed and executed some of the most magnificent examples of firehouse architecture.

In the early days of the American colonies, little thought was given to actually battling fires. So the public saw no need to create a fully staffed fire department or a facility to house it. Rather than making an effort to fight fires, energy was put into fire prevention. As early as 1638, significant efforts were made to minimize the threat of fire. Smoking tobacco was banned in Boston. New Amsterdam (later to become New York) abolished open fires between 9 P.M. and 4:30 A.M. In 1715, open flames were made illegal in Boston. Fireworks were prohibited in Newport, Rhode Island.

But what if a fire did start? What would happen if it spread, threatening homes and lives? In most cases, local citizenry were powerless to fight fires once they began. In some major cities, watchmen were hired to patrol streets at night and sound an alarm when a fire started. Bell towers were erected in other towns specifically to sound the alarm of a blaze. Some cities were organized well enough to hire an actual fire warden, who was charged with supervising fire prevention and organizing volunteer firefighters to douse fires. These strategies, however, were usually poorly planned and woefully executed.

The general plan was to demand that every able-bodied man, woman, and child respond to a fire and form two lines stretching from a well, pond, or cistern to the burning structure. One line passed buckets filled with water to douse the blaze while the other passed the empty buckets back to the source of water. These became known as bucket brigades. Unfortunately, these early attempts at firefighting were dismal failures, as buckets of water were no match for serious blazes.

Firefighting techniques were so primitive during the pre–Revolutionary War period that they could hardly be considered an antecedent to today's firefighting technology. Still, with the occasional backward step, progress was made in slow, incremental stages toward adequate fire suppression. Individuals in many towns were expected to keep a barrel full of water on their property. In Boston, each house was required to possess a 12-foot (3.7m) pole with a large swab on the end that could be dipped into

Below: The Calico ghost town near Barstow, California, preserved its firefighting equipment in the center of town, where a wooden trough provided easy access to the community's water source. These early attempts at fighting fires were failures, though; the bucket brigades rarely kept up with the flames.

Right: This early illustration of the first firefighting apparatus in Philadelphia, Pennsylvania, shows how new technology began to transform firefighting. The hand pump was a significant improvement over the largely ineffective bucket brigades.

a bucket of water and applied to a burning roof. By the mid- to late 1600s, cities like New York had leather buckets, displaying the city seal, hung outside municipal buildings and taverns. By the early nineteenth century, ladders had become a common tool for firefighting.

But the fathers of Boston, New York, and Philadelphia were growing weary of the conflagrations that were beginning to occur with sickening regularity. Every fire that began might eventually consume entire city blocks; the average fire reduced at least fifty buildings before it extinguished itself.

After one such nasty blaze leveled fifty houses in Boston, the city's aldermen began discussing ways to control these devastating fires. They considered purchasing an engine from England that had the potential of at least containing a blaze to under a city block. It was 1678, and the engine that eventually arrived on the Boston docks was a crude affair: measuring 18 by 36 inches (46 x 91cm), it looked like a large, rectangular, wooden bathtub. The new machine used a long-handled pump and a curved wooden nozzle to pump the water out. Unfortunately, it was placed not on wheels for easy transportation to a fire, but rather on poles that two men carried as they ran to a fire scene, much like stretcher bearers.

This early tub wasn't particularly advanced equipment, but it was a step in the right direction: it was mechanical and it provided a boost to complement the muscle of men. And if properly employed, this small device could save the work of two people on the fire bucket line. In the loosest sense of the word, it was perhaps the first "fire engine." Boston's new machine, however, did not translate into a flood of similar contraptions for other cities. It took Charleston, South Carolina, fifty years to order its first model, although it was a much-improved version of the old bathtub-style contraption. This newer version was placed on wooden wheels and came with a double-action pump that could be operated by either hand or foot, allowing a minimum of two men to pump water from the container. A 1731 version ordered by the city of New York was capable of pumping 170 gallons (773l) a minute and spraying a stream of water a distance of 120 feet (36.6m).

While these pumps were being developed, the first volunteer fire departments in North America were being created. Several cities lay claim to being the birthplace of the volunteer fire department, but it most likely began with the organization of the Boston Fire Association. Founded in 1717, this association was a club that served members exclusively, protecting only a fellow members' property. The Philadelphia Union Fire Company, founded by Benjamin Franklin in 1736, took a more active role in battling fires, resolving to extend assistance even to those who did not belong to the company. By the end of the century, volunteer fire departments were commonplace, and the responsibility of battling fires was taken from citizens and given to these private organizations. Yet firehouses were still a thing of the future; the necessary equipment was housed in sheds, and meetings among volunteer firefighters were held at local taverns.

Right: Major metropolitan centers suffered major fire damage due to inadequate firefighting techniques, lax fire laws, and an abundance of wooden structures built closely together. One such conflagration in Boston was captured in this drawing by W. Caister.

Left: Hand pumpers in the early and mid-nineteenth century were virtually useless when battling huge blazes such as this one in an industrial building on New York City's Duane Street.

Right: Elegant Georgian details like the pedimented doorway, windows with decorative entablatures, and dentil cornice moldings make the Friendship Fire Company a landmark in Alexandria, Virginia. Colonial buildings like this one are much more likely to have survived in small cities, where population growth was relatively slow and the buildings remained useful over long periods of time.

THE FIRST FIREHOUSES

As volunteer fire groups became more commonplace, civic leaders preferred to use these private organizations to protect their cities. In 1825, the city of Philadelphia broke up its municipal fire-watch program and turned the responsibility over to a private company that consisted of fifty firefighters. These firefighters were exempt from certain taxes, militia duty, and jury duty, and often were paid a fee for each fire they fought. Without an established firehouse, however, the groups continued meeting in local taverns.

Soon fires were being fought with early mechanical devices, which were initially left outdoors and quickly succumbed to damage from the elements. Now city leaders were faced with the problem of where to store the devices. Early firefighting companies were given the responsibility of ensuring that their equipment was protected from the weather, and the firefighters were charged with building firehouses to protect their equipment. Firehouses during this period were often nothing more than whitewashed sheds that protected equipment; these progressively became larger as the equipment became more and more sophisticated.

Left: Many early nineteenth-century fire stations, such as this structure in Medford, New Jersey, were little more than sheds designed to protect equipment from the elements.

Above: Fire engines were modern marvels of technology, and garnered interest wherever they were parked. In this archival photograph, a collection of onlookers ranging from pre-adolescent boys to businessmen inspect the rig with admiration.

Opposite: In this photograph, taken on September 12, 1917, in Stillwater, Minnesota, an old steamer is parked at the arched entrance of a livery stable. Since there is no indication that this building is an actual firehouse, this is probably a retirement picture for the steamer.

It wasn't long before equipment and men came under the same roof. Just thirteen years after the founding of the Philadelphia fire department, New York City authorities gave its Engine No. 4 its own house on Broadway, between Cedar and Fulton streets.

With dedicated quarters, often including a fireplace and comfortable furniture, came a strengthened camaraderie among the men. During their idle hours they drank and played games; after fighting fires they would return to the firehouse to tell stories. The firefighter's status was beginning to grow.

More changes were on the way in the arena of firefighting. At the dawn of the nineteenth century, buckets were generally discarded in favor of the more efficient pumps. Cast-iron, T-shaped fixtures appeared in Philadelphia to mark the first fire hydrants. Leather hoses with copper rivets were introduced to replace linen hoses that burst under pressure from improved water mains. Firefighting techniques began to gradually improve, and, with this progress, came increased prestige for the communities' firefighters.

It was a magnificent sight to see more than two dozen men moving a ponderous fire engine through muddy city streets, shouting rallying cries to urge each other on as they moved the behemoth to a fire. A trail of young boys always followed close behind, hoping to lend a hand. Once at the blaze, firefighters would quickly line up their equipment, making sure to be close to the burning structure yet still adjacent to a source of water. Ladder companies would scramble up the side of the building to rescue victims. In the center of this frenzied activity, the foreman would shout orders in cadence through a speaking trumpet to help his men pump the machine in rhythm. This remarkable entertainment rivaled anything on the stage. Poems and songs were written in tribute to the firefighter. Newspaper editorials lavished praise. In peacetime, firefighters supplanted military men as role models. They wore bright uniforms and held colorful

E.
LON DI GON,
IVERY & BOARDING STABLE
STAR
TOBACCO
FOOT-SCHULZE SHOES
FOOT-SCHULZE SHOES

Right: In his painting "The American Fireman, Prompt to the Rescue," Louis Maurer idealizes the intrepid fireman, who saves the helpless and the weak.

Far right: Classical design touches, inspired by the Greek Revival movement of the day, give this firehouse a dignified air. Built in 1862 and remodeled in 1917, the South Boston firehouse was home to Engine Co. 1 from 1868 to 1977 and Ladder Co. 5 from 1917 to 1954.

parades in city streets. In short order, the volunteer firefighter was the action hero of the nineteenth century.

Their surging popularity gave firefighters the leverage to negotiate more substantial quarters. Many cities adopted two-story brick buildings; others chose simple clapboard structures. Some towns favored granite.

Among the first distinctive firehouse styles was Greek Revival, a style that dominated American architecture between 1818 and 1850. The Greek Revival movement celebrated the Greek temple as an architectural form, embracing its simple elegance and functionality. Not limited to a specific geographical area, Greek Revival styling was applied to residences as well as to city halls, post offices, and other public buildings. Architects designing firehouses during this period took their cue from a number of sources, including the New York Custom House (1833–42), the Boston Custom House (1837–47), and the Treasury Building in Washington, D.C. (1839–69).

Right: The Old Goose Neck—an antique firefighting apparatus belonging to the Paterson, New Jersey, Fire Department—is now a museum piece.

Leading architects of the day, including Robert Mills, Ammi B. Young, and Alexander Parris, were emulated by architects in smaller cities, and the long-running trend of designing smartly styled buildings to house fire companies began in earnest.

A RESISTANCE TO CHANGE

Advances in accommodations and equipment were not always met with enthusiasm by firefighters, a resistance that tested the patience of civic leaders and ultimately tarnished the reputation of the fire companies. The steam engine is one technological advance that was at first rejected by firefighters, who saw it as a threat to their masculinity.

Invented in England and imported to North America in 1828, the steam engine was hardly embraced by firefighters on either side of the Atlantic. In fact, decades would pass before it earned their support and was welcomed as an effective firefighting tool.

While steam was the driving force behind the Industrial Revolution, and the locomotive gained wide-ranging acceptance in its infancy, the steam engine designed to fight fires was strangely viewed as less than manly. To many minds, the steam engine challenged the image of firefighters as heroes in the face of disaster.

The steamer invented by George Braithwaite and John Ericsson in London was driven by a ten-horsepower engine that contained two horizontal cylinders. It took twenty minutes to develop working pressure, and then provided enough pressure to pump

Left: During the horse-drawn era, firefighting equipment, such as this fire engine, now preserved in California's Columbia Historic State Park, became more intricate and sophisticated.

Previous: New York City firefighters battle a blaze in freezing temperatures at Broadway's Equitable Building.

Above: A steam engine gleams on a New York City street in the 1890s.

150 gallons (682l) of water per minute to a maximum height of 90 feet (27.5m). A phenomenal piece of workmanship, this engine could conceivably do the work of more than twenty men on a fire line.

The steamer proved its worth when, in the winter of 1828, during the Argyll Rooms Opera House fire in London, the manual pumps froze. Braithwaite rushed his fire engine down to the scene and put water to flame for five hours straight. Unfortunately, this feat impressed nobody.

Civic leaders complained that the engine was too powerful for the street's water mains. It would steal jobs from working firefighters. They contended that the new engines couldn't replace human muscle. But the simple truth was that it threatened the men who thought of themselves as the city's saviors.

This resistance to change was perhaps the beginning of the decline in the perception of firefighters that characterized the early nineteenth century. Because fire companies were private organizations and were not accountable to municipal leaders, some of the men began to behave in ways that tarnished the image of the firefighter. The fire station, once a comfortable meeting place and clubhouse, became more of a neighborhood saloon. A new generation of firefighters lacked the same high principles of their predecessors, and looked at fighting fires as a sport rather than a calling or even a job. Parades, banquets, and drinking became their priorities; fighting fires came in a distant second. Firehouses began to attract young hoodlums. Fire organizations also began to form along ethnic lines. Frequently, two fire groups would battle it out in the streets over who had the right to fight the fire, even as a building blazed nearby, often to the ground.

Below: A two-horse fire wagon pulls members of the New York City Fire Department.

Right: Insurance companies employed firefighters in the nineteenth century, and buildings were often marked with the company's logo. In advertisements circa 1890, the Triumph Insurance Company of Chicago used a depiction of the great Chicago Fire of 1871.

These battles became so commonplace that the public came to expect little of the fire units, often assuming that no building would be saved. But they became more alarmed when these street fights erupted into full-scale riots, leaving firefighters and innocent bystanders dead. In one incident, a fistfight between a Boston firefighter and an Irish immigrant escalated to a riot when Boston firefighters retaliated, ransacking houses in an Irish neighborhood.

Unfortunately, while the violence escalated, the fires continued to blaze out of control. Seventeen blocks in lower Manhattan were leveled by fire in 1835. Nine hundred buildings were destroyed in Pittsburgh in 1845. A fire in Albany in 1848 killed thirty-eight people. In 1850, six hundred structures burned to the ground in Philadelphia. Insurance companies were becoming impatient with the large claims, and business owners were alarmed over the rising insurance premiums that inevitably followed such payments.

The difficulties continued until, in the early 1850s, the volunteer fire department was dealt a significant blow, a result of their own behavior. A Cincinnati wood mill was destroyed in 1851 when firefighters ignored the flames and instead attempted to beat back the firefighters from neighboring cities who had arrived to help. Six men were killed and the mill was a total loss. A campaign by city officials led to the elimination of the volunteer fire department and the creation of a paid municipal department, the United States' first fully staffed and paid fire department.

But Cincinnati's elders weren't satisfied with just a paid staff. They wanted effective equipment to complement their new professional firefighters, and they commissioned Abel Shawk and Alexander Bonner Latta to develop a steam fire engine specifically for their fire department.

Steam engine manufacturing companies were already in existence. Pain & Caldwell, a steam engine builder, had been founded in 1839 in Seneca Falls, New York, which became the center of production for this new machine. Silsby Manufacturing Company, which would become the leader of the industry, set up shop in 1861; Rumsey & Company in 1864; Gleason & Bailey in 1884; and the American Fire Engine Company in 1891.

But Cincinnati's commissioning of a steam engine was a turning point in firefighting history, and the decision received a boost on New Year's Day, 1853. On that day, a competition was held between a hand-pumping crew from the Union Fire Company of Cincinnati and the new steam-powered pumper. The Union crew was exhausted within a half hour. The new steamer, however, gave an impressive display of power by producing six 225-foot (68.6m) streams of water at the same time. Firefighters, of course, were less than enthralled and attempted to sabotage it. But the steamer proved too effective to ignore. The end of human strength as the sole means of fighting a fire was in sight.

As cities across North America moved quickly to establish paid fire departments, the steam engine followed. Firefighters insisted on moving the equipment

Below: Cincinnati's pioneering steam-powered engine was an elaborate, Rube Goldberg–style contraption that was nonetheless far more effective than the old hand pumpers.

Below: The chief of the Seattle, Washington, Fire Department sits in his carriage at headquarters sometime between 1897 and 1900.

themselves, however, refusing the addition of horses to their team. It was hardly a rational decision, since the equipment was extremely heavy and difficult to move, especially during the winter months when roads were often wet, muddy, or buried beneath a foot of snow. When city aldermen proposed employing horses to move steam engines, firefighters balked. Already suspicious of the technology associated with the steam engine, they refused to share their beloved firehouses with horses. But the pressure to accept horses to haul equipment was immense. As the political clout of volunteer fire departments waned and paid firefighters were hired and held accountable to the mayor's office and city aldermen, firefighters realized they had little choice but to accept horses in the firehouse. By the 1870s, horses were a common part of the firefighting team.

With horse-drawn steam engines now part of the city landscape, firehouses grew to enormous proportions. A typical two-story firehouse in New York City consisted of floor space measuring about 15 feet (4.6m) wide and as much as 30 feet (9.1m) long to accommodate hook-and-ladder trucks. The equipment was stored at the front of the building behind huge bay doors, while the horses were quartered in stalls near the rear. (Horses were initially quartered behind the firehouse, but it took too long to bring the animals to the equipment, so they were moved closer.) Behind the horse stalls was a harness room and a storage bin for hay and feed. Older equipment might be stored at the rear of the building in a shed. On the second floor was the bunk room, private quarters for the chief and foreman, and a wash room that contained a bath and a toilet. Firehouses were further enlarged when alarm systems, which required a room for the board and equipment, were installed.

Above: In snow-bound Quebec, firefighters used equipment placed on runners to transport fire hoses to an alarm.

The Horse: A Beloved Member of the Fire Company

When Fire Horse Fred died in the harness pulling a crew to a false alarm in 1925, the men of New Bern, North Carolina, were grief-stricken. Fred had pulled the fire hose wagon for seventeen years. In tribute, the firefighters had Fred's head stuffed and mounted. In 1957, it found a new home in the Fireman's Museum, where it remains today.

There is nothing curious or morbid about Fred's head. Horses were a much-loved part of a firefighter's life, at times even more respected than their bunkmates. Horses were often better fed and better cared for than the men who drove them to alarms. The firefighters took as much care when grooming their glistening coats and brushing their manes as they did when spit-shine polishing the steam engines that trailed them.

Although the surging popularity of paid fire departments during the late nineteenth and early twentieth centuries was due in large part to the professionalism of the firefighters and their ability to prevent and fight fires, the role of the horse cannot be denied. There probably wasn't a single child, or adult for that matter, who didn't look upon the firefighter with deep affection because of his four-legged partner. Although firefighters were viewed as tough and masculine, their horses made them seem compassionate and vulnerable as well. The humanity of the firefighter was best seen in the way he treated his horses.

Above: During the horse's long service to fire departments, it was virtually deified by firefighters.

Below: In 1904, conditions were primitive in Nome, Alaska, but the small fire department there sported a two-horse wagon to pull its chemical engine to fires.

The fire horse underwent a grueling training program rivaling that of the firefighter. Major metropolitan centers, such as Detroit, had fire horse academies specifically designed to train horses not only for that city's fire department but also for departments from neighboring cities and even other states. Horses that successfully completed training courses possessed the necessary stamina, skill, and even talent to pull steamers and support wagons through crowded city streets in just minutes.

All horses were assigned a station and given either a number or, more often, a name. Horses fell into three categories. The lightweight horse, which weighed about 1,100 pounds (500kg), was employed on hose wagons. The middleweight, at 1,400 pounds (635.6kg), pulled the steamers. And the heavyweight horse, at 1,700 pounds (771.8kg), hauled the hook-and-ladder wagons and other heavy equipment. The horses knew their roles well, often positioning themselves under their suspended harnesses at the sound of an alarm. A good team of horses could move from stall to harness to street in less than three minutes.

Because agility and strength were key to a crack team, draft horses were almost always selected for firefighting duty. Decended from the horses of the Perche region of France, the horses most often used for firefighting were a cross of Arabian and Turkish blood mixed with that of Flemish draft horses. Over the centuries, these horses wrer bred into huge, sturdy animals. By the 1870s, Percherons were already imported in large numbers from ranches, and were employed for heavy farm work, in delivery service, and

Above: A firefighting crew poses with their assembled steeds. Though firefighters were initially reluctant to accept horses into the firehouse, many firefighters wept when their beloved teammates were finally phased out of duty by the early 1920s.

as circus entertainment. But the Percheron draft horse found its true calling pulling fire equipment.

The draft horse seemed unstoppable. One often-told story involved Jim, the Beau Brummel, a popular draft horse at the Toledo (Ohio) Fire Department. Considered the handsomest horse of the department, the dapple gray and beautifully marked equine was the strongest and most intelligent horse on the team. Just seven years old in 1912 and with the department only two years, Jim had one exceptionally busy day in the lead position of the three-horse hitch. He had responded to eight alarms in the course of the day and was being hitched for the ninth when his driver noticed that his left hind leg was broken. It was never known how many alarms Jim had responded to with the broken leg, but he was still snorting eagerly to do his ninth call. Jim had become such a legend in the department that an official departmental portrait was commissioned. It was still being painted when he died, and it survives today.

In Oklahoma City, Jumbo and Babe, bought together for $250, became immediate celebrities. The horses were famous for being able to distinguish between the ring of a regular phone and the firehouse's fire phone. When the fire phone rang, the horses would leap to their hitch straps, often before the phone could be answered. On one occasion, the fire phone rang and Jumbo and Babe stampeded to their harnesses. Firefighters slid down the poles and the driver jumped onto the apparatus as another firefighter fastened the harnesses. But as Jumbo and Babe charged from the firehouse, the startled driver discovered that his reins were not attached to the animals. It made no difference: Jumbo and Babe smelled the smoke and raced unerringly to the scene of the fire.

Across town at Station No. 1, horses George, Dank Joe, and Pat were a team that were probably unparalleled in their ability to get to a fire quickly. When Pat died, station members provided him with a funeral to rival that of any human firefighter. Firefighters stenciled the words "Old Pat Has Gone to His Last Run" on the side of the hearse that carried him through town in an elaborate procession.

When it became inevitable that motorized apparatus was soon to replace the horse, firefighters were loathe to accept the gasoline-powered fire engine. Firefighters were known to hate change, but this time there was an emotional component as well. They weren't simply suspicious, as they had been with the steamer; this time they had grown attached to their horses and were not ready to let go. Some men quit the fire department, remarking that fighting fires was no longer fun without their beloved horses.

The San Francisco City and County Municipal Record noted the passing of the horse in its October 15, 1925, edition: "Hardly a vestige of the horse-drawn period remains in the City. It has disappeared even more completely than the earlier hand-drawn apparatus which was light enough to be housed and kept as souvenirs. The massive steamer is no more. Gasoline has taken the place of coal. The motor has driven the horse from the field of activity in man's behalf."

Below: Harnesses hung from the ceiling, dropping automatically as firefighters guided their horses underneath them. Many horses were so well trained that, at the sound of an alarm, they ran on their own to the harness.

FIREFIGHTING TECHNOLOGY ADVANCES

During a hectic thirty-year period before the end of the nineteenth century, firefighters discovered new ways to shave off time from the moment the alarm sounded to the moment they arrived at a blaze. Once firefighters accepted the horses, they perfected ways to harness them quickly. The most common feature was the "hanging harness," which hung above the horse in its stall. When an alarm sounded, the harness could be dropped onto the back of the horse and locked into place beneath its belly. When firehouses were wired for electricity, the harness became wired to the alarm and dropped automatically when the alarm sounded.

Another time-saving invention was the legendary sliding pole. In the late 1870s, a unit of black firefighters at Station 21 in Chicago found quick access from their second-floor quarters to the ground-floor equipment by sliding down from the hay loft on one of the support poles. Captain David Kenyon decided to expand on the idea by sanding down a wooden pole, working oil into the surface, and placing it into a hole cut in the bunk room floor. The first pole was officially in place. Brass

Above: In this staged 1943 photograph, taken in Washington, D.C., at Fire Station No. 4, firefighters demonstrate how they rush to their trucks in response to an alarm.

poles later replaced wooden versions. Like the horse harness, the disk that covered the sliding pole was wired to the alarm, allowing the disk to shoot up as soon as the alarm sounded. The sliding pole knocked off even more precious seconds in getting the firefighter to the scene of a blaze.

As these changes took place, the horse, at first only reluctantly accepted, became an essential part of every fire company. For more than fifty years, horses were integral members of the firefighting team, and were embraced and loved like any colleague. And these animals performed beyond the call of duty. For passersby on the street, the height of excitement was watching a three-horse team rush by, pulling a steam engine at full boil. But with the popularity that motorized trucks gained during World War I, the era of the horse-driven steamer came to a close. Capable of hauling huge loads, the trucks also operated at a fraction of the cost of maintaining a horse.

DAN

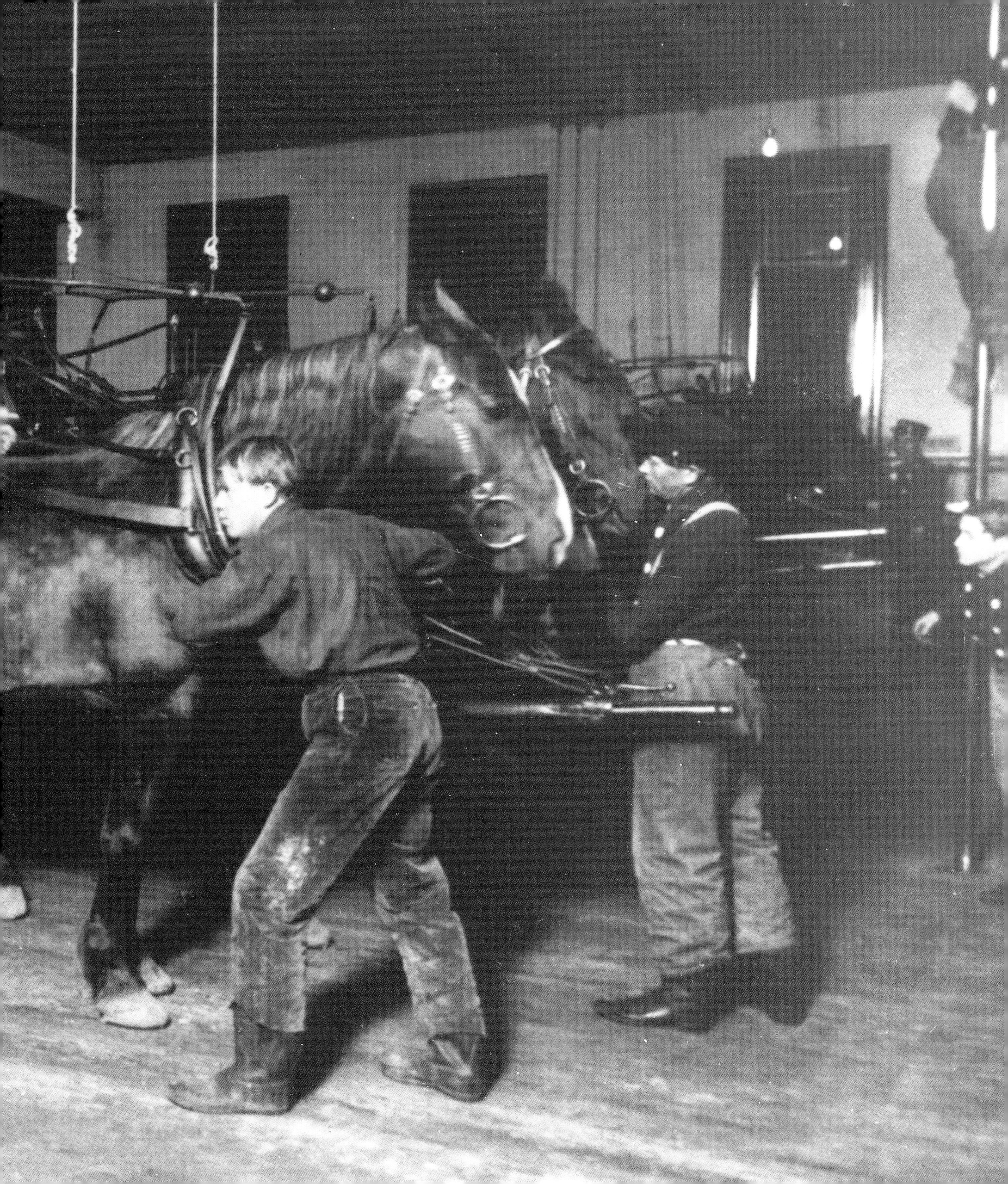

Previous: This demonstration illustrates how horses are harnessed.

Above: The Pleasantville Fire Department typifies many small town firehouses with its simple two-story wooden structure.

Right: The 1922 Seagrave hose truck was considered the best firefighting equipment in post-World War I America.

Between 1920 and 1923, cities beefed up their motorized units and sent their horses to pasture.

Cities across the continent held ceremonial "last call" fire alarms to race their horses at breakneck speeds through the streets. Thousands of residents lined the streets to watch these proud animals make one last display of raw power. For those who grew up in awe of these magnificent workers, it was an emotional moment, and signalled the end of an era.

TAHOE CITY
Volunteer Fire Dept.
1
CALIFORNIA
69743
NORTH LAKE TAHOE

The Alarm Office

When the Toldeo Fire Department's alarm office was completed in December 1930, it featured state-of-the-art technology. The building's impressive architecture befitted the stature that the alarm office held within municipal government.

City architects designed the three-story building in the Colonial style, with the lower floor faced with Bedford stone and the upper stories laid with red brick and trimmed in Bedford stone. The cupola was covered in copper and the dome atop the building was made of lead. The cupola served as one of the supports for the radio broadcasting antenna. It was probably the most elaborate alarm office in the country, a monument to ever-changing firefighting technology.

While the traditional firehouse is the heart and soul of the fire department, the alarm office is the brains. Today, 800 MHz radios transmit fire and rescue calls from a vast communications center to outlying firehouses, dispatching emergency crews within minutes, if not seconds, to a call. The road to this vast network was paved with incremental changes in the way calls for fire service were relayed from the people of the community to the firehouse.

The fire alarm office can trace its roots to Samuel F. B. Morse's invention of the telegraph in 1844. Less than a year after the telegraph emerged as a communication system, Dr. William F. Channing of Boston proposed, in an essay in the *Boston Daily Advertiser*, that a practical fire alarm system could be constructed, based on the technology of the telegraph, that would save time, property, and lives. It took Channing six years, however, to convince the city of Boston to fund the construction of an alarm system. But once in place, the system gained widespread popularity among other municipal governments, and by the time the Civil War ended in 1865, most major metropolitan cities had some form of alarm telegraph system.

Boston's first fire alarm office was housed in the City Building at Court Square and Williams Court. It debuted in 1852 and its staff included a superintendent, fire alarm operators, and repairmen. These were the first positions of their kind within a fire department. The original system consisted of nineteen alarm bells and forty street boxes on three box circuits. All of the boxes were manual crank type with locked outside doors, painted black.

As explained by the San Francisco Fire Department in 1865, typical instructions for a fire alarm box were:

> Upon the discovery of a fire near your signal box, turn the crank slowly and steadily about 25 or 30 times, then wait a few moments, and, if you hear no ticking in the box, or alarm on the bells, turn as before. If you still hear no alarm, go to the next box and give the alarm from that. Never open the box or touch the crank, except in case of fire. Never signal for a fire seen at a distance. Be sure your box is locked before leaving it.

Generally, each city possessed a different alarm system. Larger cities usually laid out aerial—and later underground—wires to various boxes around the city at strategic locations. As cities grew in the latter nineteenth and early twentieth centuries, the lines were placed farther and farther from a central fire alarm office. Most cities used an independent power source for alarm boxes to guard against power outages caused by a major disaster. Alarm offices generally furnished enough power for emergency lighting and for charging batteries. Early on, alarm boxes acted much like electrical switches, although they were mechanical in operation. The fire department would routinely test all the boxes about once a month by winding them, much like an alarm clock. This would allow each box to transmit as many as twenty separate alarms.

Typically, alarm boxes were connected to a complex apparatus system in a central office. The system included a cable terminal in the basement and operating boards, central desk, a telephone switchboard, and power and lighting circuit control boards in the main office. Types and styles of alarm boxes varied, and each box was numbered, signifying its location. In the city of Toledo, Ohio, for example, boxes were assigned number groups to represent various sections of the city. The 400 series would be located in the northern portion of the city; the 500 and 700 series on the east side; the 600 series covered a another specific area; and the 800 series covered west Toledo. When an alarm was sounded, it was transmitted to the fire alarm office, where an operator would throw a switch on the receiving circuit. The switch connected a relay repeater, which would transmit the box number to firehouses. The operation was so elaborate (and remains so even today)

that it required its own building. During the early years, alarm offices were housed in larger city firehouses, often taking up an entire floor of its own. But as cities grew, the systems also grew, and eventually alarm offices required buildings of their own.

Between the end of the Civil War and the dawn of the twentieth century, many municipalities relied on private business to keep and maintain alarm boxes, but this proved to be an awkward relationship. The city of Toledo was hampered by its contract with the American District Telegraph Company in the late nineteenth century. The telegraph company had hammered out an agreement with the city of Toledo to place its own fire alarm boxes on poles on corners in business districts. The key to the locked box would be placed in the care of a merchant or business owner. If a passerby wanted to report a fire, he was required to go into the business and ask for the key, then unlock the box and pull the crank on the box. This itself might cost several seconds, but the real problem occurred when fires were spotted at night. Since businesses were closed, the reporting party had to track down the business owner at his residence to retrieve the key. Precious minutes were lost, resulting in loss of life and property.

The city of Toledo decided to strike out on its own and ordered 258 fire alarm boxes, a manual transmitter, and relays from the Gamewell Company. A telephone switchboard was purchased from the Western Electric Company. The city then converted the second-floor rear area of Station No. 3 Engine House to its fire alarm office in January 1899. Many other cities followed suit.

Advancing technology created changes in the alarm office operation at a rapid pace. Telephone switchboards were beginning to appear in the early 1880s. Cities such as Boston began installing telephone systems to complement their fire alarm box operations. By the early 1890s, cities in the Northeast were growing so fast that fire departments began installing boxes in the suburbs. By 1928, radios arrived in firehouses to supplement boxes and telephones. Fire engines and fire officers' cars were also equipped with radios. In 1938, the city of Columbus, Ohio, installed a public address system that allowed each call to be broadcast to all firehouses after an alarm was called in. Mobile communications centers arrived in the early 1940s. Computerized dispatch systems were commonplace by 1985, and 1991 saw the debut of 800MHz radios that allowed several talk groups on a single fire department's radio system, thus enhancing mutual aid calls.

Fire alarm offices have developed into computerized hi-tech nerve centers that, in effect, play the role of guardians of life and property. In a profession not known for its advanced thinking during its formative years, firefighting nonetheless seized an opportunity to exploit the new technology of telegraphs, and in so doing helped save many lives.

Opposite: At New Hampshire's Mount Hale, an operator at the fire observatory alerts headquarters to a fire. The clock atop the telephone allows the observer to mark the specific time of the call.

Left: Alarm boxes such as these are ubiquitous in public buildings across the country.

Below: Firefighter Henry Fisher takes an emergency call in a fire department's alarm room. In the early twentieth century, many fire stations had to be expanded or remodeled to accommodate the alarm room.

Above: An integral part of the community, firefighters help kids in Minneapolis, Minnesota, beat the summer heat.

Right: In many communities, volunteer firefighters took their jobs very seriously. Here, a young Jersey City volunteer, circa 1890, poses in dress uniform with a speaking trumpet, used to shout orders over the din at the scene.

Opposite: With a little tutoring, a fireman in St. Paul, Minnesota, knits a sock for a soldier in World War I.

FIRE DEPARTMENT
71
CHICAGO
FIRE DEPT.

The Firehouse Heart of the Town

Firehouses, key landmarks in virtually every neighborhood across the continent, reflect the tastes and social customs that prevailed at the time they were constructed. Most vintage firehouses that remain standing were built between the end of the Civil War and the end of World War II, and were designed as both practical and symbolic structures; they provided necessary housing for men and equipment and they inspired confidence and pride with their imposing presences.

While few firehouses were built by premier architects, many possess the signature elements found in buildings created by leading architects such as Henry Hobson Richardson, with his emphasis on fortress-style structures, and Julia Morgan, who often used Mission or Spanish Revival. Greatly influenced by five hundred years of European architecture, North American architecture was often a combination of many different styles and techniques, some borrowed from the Old Country and others fresh innovations. Nature-inspired, curvilinear Art Nouveau touches complemented—but also disdained—the conventions of Victorian architecture, a collection of movements that had in common a tendency toward excess. Massive Romanesque edifices recall medieval fortresses, and the streamlined, geometrical look of Art Deco, inspired in part by advances in industrial design, was applied as well, presaging the modern designs that appeared later in the twentieth century.

Previous: Engine Co. 71 is one of ninety-eight engine companies in the Chicago Fire Department, the largest fire department in the Midwest, serving nearly three million people.

Left: A well-designed firehouse complements the surrounding neighborhood. Exposed brick, a mansard roof, and a tower complete with a cupola for drying hoses set this firehouse apart from the other structures, but keep it within the theme of the neighborhood.

IMPOSING EDIFICES

When early-nineteenth-century civic leaders considered designs for municipal buildings, they chose imposing structures that invoked the classical tradition, which called to mind the ideals of egalitarianism and democracy. Greek Revival emerged as an adaptable style that could be applied to a variety of buildings. The Ohio State Capital in Columbus (1838–61) and such commercial buildings as the Quincy Market in Boston (1825–26) set the standard for Greek Revival architecture. The Greek Revival style came to embody the quintessential government building, seen at its grandest in the Treasury Building in Washington, D.C., and the Custom House of New York City. State, and local municipalities emulated these noble buildings on a smaller scale for state capitol buildings and city halls.

Right: Built in 1869, this firehouse in the Dorchester section of Boston is built primarily in the Second Empire style, which shares certain detailing with the Italianate style. The mansard roof and pedimented dormer windows are hallmarks of Second Empire, named after the reign of France's Napoleon III.

The firehouse, in terms of size and relative importance to the community, was deemed less important than city hall, but was nevertheless designed to command respect from citizens, and many were constructed on the Greek Revival model. Few Greek Revival firehouses survive today, but the tendency for firehouse design to follow national trends in both government and commercial architecture endured for more than one hundred years.

In the years immediately following the Civil War, the firehouse was seen by municipal architects as an opportunity to experiment with cutting edge design. Flourishes not being applied to other public or commercial buildings were often incorporated into firehouse exteriors. Perhaps buildings such as city halls and customs houses were expected to remain conservative, in keeping with the serious business being conducted inside, while firehouses, which housed only a small company of men and horses, could afford to be more daring in appearance.

One thing that set the firehouse apart from the usual commercial building was its size. The typical firehouse now accommodated as many as six horses, with feed and equipment to service them, in addition to large steamers and ladder trucks. By necessity, firehouses were enormous, giving them a significance in the community not found in residences or commercial buildings.

By the 1850s the Italianate style had emerged as an alternative to popular Greek Revival designs. With their vertical proportions, tall, rounded windows and doors, and intricately patterned stone trim, Italianate buildings exuded the warmth and character of a country villa. Because the style was easily applied to square constructions, it was particularly simple to maximize space and adapt buildings to standard city lots, and thus the Italianate style became a natural choice for urban areas.

When the city of Richmond, Virginia, rebuilt its Steamer No. 5 firehouse in 1863, it sought to establish warm tones and move away from the heavy lines found in

42 ENGINE 42
5 CHEMICAL 5

227 ENGINE
ONE WAY

Opposite, Top Left: The curved bay—which connects two separated segments of this Queens, New York, firehouse—subtly suggests a Victorian tower, a popular element in 1892, when this station was built.

Opposite, Top Right: As the neighborhoods changed, so too did the firehouses. The same Queens firehouse, after a 1927 renovation and the construction of an elevated train in the foreground, continues to blend with an increasingly eclectic neighborhood.

Opposite, Bottom: In urban areas, the firehouse was not always a community centerpiece, largely due to spatial constraints. In this photograph of a 1930s-era Brooklyn neighborhood, the fire station is tightly sandwiched between residential housing.

Left: Typical of Queen Anne–style townhouses, the elaborate brick and masonry patterning and scuptural medallions of this 1902 New York City firehouse offer the much-desired impression of textured wall space.

Right: Rough-faced, squared stonework is the main feature of this 1898 firehouse in Calumet, Michigan. Its massive, fortress-like appearance is in keeping with its Richardsonian Romanesque styling.

Opposite, Top: The stepped parapet of the Calumet fire station creates a ziggurat-like pattern against the sky.

Opposite, Bottom: The Greek Revival styling of this Sacramento, California, firehouse is unusual for the West, though it was a favorite style in Eastern cities. Most firehouses on the West Coast were designed in Romanesque, Victorian, or, occasionally, Prairie style. The Old Sacramento Fire Station No. 3 was built in 1853 and housed a restaurant in the 1970s.

most municipal buildings of the era. By adapting an Italianate design, with its heavy overhanging cornices and rich but simple trim carvings of brick and brownstone, Richmond signaled that it was trading in the whitewashed walls and rigid presentation of Greek Revival for a more inviting design. As early as 1848, the city of Boston experimented with the Italianate style for Torrent No. 6 station, as did Mobile, Alabama, with its Phoenix Engine Company firehouse.

Contemporary with the Italianate style is Second Empire, a favorite style for American houses and public buildings during the Grant administration, which lasted from 1869 to 1877. While architects working in the Italianate style gained inspiration from the Romantic villas of Italy, architects championing the Second Empire style drew from modern vogues in French buildings. A primary characteristic of Second Empire buildings is the distinctive mansard roof. This was a particularly attractive feature, as the roof's boxy silhouette allowed for maximum attic space. Second Empire and Italianate buildings share many decorative details, such as arched, segmentally arched, or rectangular windows and doors, often with pediments or elaborate framing.

While Italianate and Second Empire designs displayed the architectural community's taste for daring, a generation later, architects adopted the Romanesque style, glorying in the sheer strength of its lines. Influenced by French and Spanish designs of the eleventh century, the Romanesque style provided a somber but impressive presence. Borrowing Byzantine and Eastern elements, these massive masonry structures often incorporated single or twin towers.

The Romanesque designs of architect Henry Hobson Richardson became so popular in the last third of the nineteenth century that the style became known as "Richardsonian Romanesque." Born in 1838, Richardson studied at Harvard, then at the Ecole des Beaux-Arts in

Right: Public buildings in the more rural areas of the West were often simple, utilitarian, wooden structures, such as this City Hall and Firehouse in Index, Washington.

Opposite: The steeply pitched roof of this 1891 Auburn, California, firehouse displays the decorative shingling so popular on Victorian buildings, and features dormers facing in each direction.

FIRE DEPT
INDEX WASH

Right: The Hagerstown, Maryland, Fire Department's firehouse features distinctive Italianate architecture with exposed brick, arched windows, and decorative brackets along the cornice line—all topped off with a bell tower.

Left: A Richardsonian Romanesque arch, springing characteristically from ground level, harbors a mechanized member of Engine Co. 33.

Paris. While in France, he worked under Henri Labrouste and Jakob Ignaz Hittorf. With Romanesque styling as his foundation, he developed his own form, characterized by massive stone walls and dramatic semicircular arches. For many of his buildings, he favored light brown granite with a dark red brownstone trim. One of his acknowledged masterpieces is Quincy, Massachusetts' Crane Memorial Public Library (1880–83), which features an entrance with a stair turret, an off-center Syrian arch, and triple arches in the top gable. Richardson died at the age of forty-eight, leaving behind a legacy that influenced other leading architects of the day, including Louis Sullivan and John Wellborn Root.

Right: Built in 1860 and remodeled in 1916 to accommodate motorized fire engines, this red brick Boston firehouse incorporates Greek Revival elements, though that style had largely faded by the 1860s. A front door topped with a decorative pediment supported by pilasters and symmetrically placed windows and doors contribute to the Classical look of the station.

Due in part to its robust quality and earnest funtionalism the Richardsonian Romanesque style continued as an influence on North American firehouse design throughout the rest of the nineteenth century. Columbus, Ohio, embraced the Romanesque theme with vigor by building six firehouses in varations of the style. Employing distinctive Richardsonian Romanesque styling, architect John Flynn designed Station No. 5 on Thurman Avenue in 1891–92. Now a popular restaurant, the vintage firehouse is constructed of brick and stone, and features a stunning tower capped with a battlement. The main portion of the building is topped with a mansard roof.

Given the fortresslike construction of buildings in the Romanesque style, it's no wonder that many firehouses in Columbus survive today. Station No.10, built in 1896 and still standing on West Broad Street, features a tower at the end of the structure with a gabled roof and pinnacle. Its façade presents a series of arched and circular windows with a parapet on top. Station No. 7, constructed in 1888, stands at the corner of Euclid and Pearl streets. Its angular tower topped with battlements and a gabled roof resembles an old-fashioned belfry.

Another example of Romanesque design is found in Bellows Falls, Vermont, where the Old Fire Station still stands. Built in 1904, the three-story load-bearing

Left: Architects designed this structure to complement surrounding buildings, but gave it enough presence to make it stand out among its neighbors. In use through 1951, this Boston fire station was constructed of stone and brick, and features numerous balconies as well as a conservative cornice at the rooftop. Not to be underdone, the designer pushed the limits with an elaborate hose drying tower featuring sturdy battlements.

Above: The Seattle, Washington, Fire Department, circa 1900, shows the influence of Victorian Stick style in its steep, gabled roof and wooden wall cladding.

Opposite: Spindlework and gingerbread trim reflect a Victorian sensibility in the Nevada City, California, firehouse.

structure features granite and decorative brickwork detailing. Part of the building's character derives from the archictect's use of mixed window shapes, semicircular openings with granite sills and keystones on the second floor, and mixed window sashes. Four years after it was built, this station began housing larger equipment, including a horse-drawn chemical wagon and a hook-and-ladder wagon. The front entrance had to be altered a few years later to accommodate two motorized fire engines.

VICTORIAN MAJESTY

While Romanesque architecture exuded massive strength, much other architecture of the Victorian era was almost dainty in its execution. The Victorian period is technically defined by the reign of England's Queen Victorian, from 1837 to 1901, and "Victorian" is actually a broad term for a collection of distinct styles that were popular during that period. Perhaps the styles most

TIQUES

Below: A firehouse in Cape May, New Jersey, now a museum, features the quaint styling common during the Victorian era.

Opposite: Built in 1868, this eclectic structure was home to Boston's Engine Co. 1 until 1977.

identified with the Victorian era are Queen Anne, which featured high-pitched roofs, ornamental shingles, decorative woodwork, and wrap-around porches, and Gothic Revival, which featured irregular plans, gables, castellated parapets, and arched windows. Northern California municipalities were especially fond of these designs; San Francisco, in particular, incorporated elaborate Queen Anne styling into many of its fire stations.

Not until after the Civil War did the Victorian designs became excessively complicated, producing a strong visual effect that has often been attacked as cluttered and fussy. While most people identify Victorian style with residential design, cities began embracing Victorian themes as a natural progression of style for their municipal buildings.

Fire officials in major metropolitan areas wielded tremendous influence in the years immediately following the Civil War. New York City was perhaps the most important municipal government organization in North America during this time, and William Marcy "Boss" Tweed and the Tammany Hall Machine reigned supreme in control of the city's government. Tweed and his minions would ultimately swindle the city out of as much as $200 million over a six-year period. His administration was also known for doling out municipal jobs by the hundreds to political cronies. In an era before firefighters were hired through written civil service tests and physical exams, jobs were handed out as favors. And when the beneficiary of a political boss spoke, government officials listened.

While Victorian firehouse architecture cannot be tied to the corruption and graft found in many municipal governments, in some respects the architeture of the era is in keeping with the other excesses of the time. Fire chiefs wanted massive monuments that honored their brave firefighters, and mayors and aldermen wanted landmark buildings that immortalized their own grand legacies.

Firemen's Hall in Ann Arbor, Michigan, is one early example of such Victorian majesty, albeit on a more subdued level than later examples. In keeping with the Victorian love of pattern, texture, and color, the Ann Arbor hall was constructed of red brick held together with black-tinted mortar; colored slate gave the façade a three-dimensional appearance. Simple but elegant corniced eaves and a spiked, cast-iron railing topped a mansard roof that capped a tower. The architect of the Ann Arbor Fireman's

WASHINGTON POST 32 G.A.R.
SPANISH WAR VETERANS
GETTYSBURG COMD No 19
UNION VETERANS UNION.

Right: These lounging firefighters in Carson City, Nevada, circa 1940 look more like high-stakes gamblers than cribbage-players.

Left: Firehouses in the nineteenth century often served more as a men's clubhouse than a center for firefighting activity. Men paid dues, held meetings, and elected officers much like any other civic organizations. The origin of this photo, showing firemen playing a game of cards, is unknown.

Following pages: This undated photograph of a Houston, Texas, firehouse displays geometric elements of Art Deco styling surrounding the bay doors, although the photo was almost certainly taken before Art Deco became popular.

Hall moved the tower—a feature that was originally added to firehouses as a means to dry hoses and so was traditionally placed at the rear of the building for efficiency—to the front of the building for the sake of visual appeal.

Interiors matched the lavishness of exterior design. Fire chiefs often complained that their firefighters had no place to read or relax. Early stations contained sleeping quarters but no lounge. Since rules prohibited firefighters from lounging in their sleeping quarters, they were forced to gather outside or near the stables. It wasn't particularly good public relations to have idle firefighters sitting around out on the street, so chiefs lobbied city officials to expand existing two-story firehouses to three floors in order to create space for a reading room and meeting area. The move was swiftly adopted. However, some fire chiefs vetoed the idea of a lounge, reasoning that if the men spent their free time eating and relaxing they would lose their edge, not to mention get flabby. Instead, these chiefs had gymnasiums installed and physical fitness instructors were brought in to keep firefighters fit.

Coinciding with the popularity of Queen Anne and other Victorian styles was Chateauesque style. This style was relatively rare for homes, as the detailing required was prohibitively expensive, but it was adopted for mansions as well as for public buildings. Chateauesque buildings feature eclectic motifs such as irregular roof lines, steeply pitched gables, and multiple tall chimneys, and owe their inspiration primarily to fourteenth- and fifteenth-century French and, later, Quebecois chateaux. Magnificent Chateauesque structures, the centerpieces of many cities, among them New York and Boston, were often copied from famed mansions such as the palatial Fifth Avenue home of William K. Vanderbilt.

In 1895, New York architects Napoleon LeBrun and Sons were commissioned to design Engine 31's new home. The goal was to create a building that

7

EP'T.
7

Above: Constructed in 1873, this firehouse is Romanesque in feel, but it presages Queen Anne styling with its pitched roof and gables.

reflected the city's expansive nature at the close of the nineteenth century, and the style chosen was elaborate Chateauesque. The resulting monogrammed gables and emblematic torches made this firehouse an anomaly among the less fanciful buildings in the neighborhood, but it succeeded in its goal.

The Buffalo, New York, Fire Department also incorporated Chateauesque influences into its firehouse for Engine 26. While not nearly as ostentatious as the New York Chateauesque structure built for Engine 31, its brick and stamped iron elements were nonetheless striking.

THE APPROACH OF THE MODERN ERA

As the twentieth century dawned, the economy remained healthy, but design became less flashy, and the need to display wealth, especially when housing municipal employees, had diminished. A new generation of architects with a more minimalist approach appeared. Although this new trend, which would emerge as the Prairie style, would eventually find a home in municipal design, its popularity really took hold with residential architecture.

Frank Lloyd Wright led this minimalist approach in a movement that would become legendary, influencing generations of architects. Wright began his career as a draftsman for J.L. Silsbee in Chicago. In 1887, he started working for Louis Sullivan, where he remained until 1893. During the last three years of his tenure under Sullivan, he handled many residential commissions and began to develop his own style. Once he went solo, it became clear that Wright's residential work was influenced by Silsbee and Sullivan. He took advantage of large design budgets by experimenting with a number of styles, but he was most at home with the minimalist

Below: The Milwaukee, Wisconsin, Fire Department favored the bungalow style—together with Prairie style, it was part of the larger Arts and Crafts Movement. This firehouse, built in 1928, integrates easily into a cozy tree-lined neighborhood.

Friedrich
CHARLESTON FIRE DEPARTMENT
3
3
E-ONE

CHARLESTON FIRE DEPARTMENT
2

approach; his philosophy was to produce structures based on organic simplicity. Wright's 1893 William Winslow residence in River Forest, Illinois, is an early example of Prairie styling. The home's signature elements—features that came to be hallmarks of the Prairie style—include a low hipped roof, broad overhanging eaves, and second-story windows placed directly under the eaves.

The Prairie-style era was relatively short-lived, lasting from about 1900 to 1920, but the clean lines and simple plans inherent to the style are present in Modern architecture as well. Prairie exteriors were generally constructed of either plaster with wood trim or horizontal board and batten siding. Soon, municipal architects began to incorporate elements of Prairie style into their designs. Rather than expand on the Victorian theme, which essentially had run its course by the turn of the cen-

Previous: A leading feature of Richardsonian Romanesque architecture, the rounded arch is prominently displayed at this Charleston, South Carolina, firehouse.

Far Left: The clean, overtly geometrical lines of Kansas City's Fire Station No. 27 shine through the dusk. Well-lit apparatus bays show the range of equipment housed at this station, home to the city's Hazardous Materials Division, formed in 1989.

Left: Squad Co. 1 in Brooklyn, New York, is now housed in the former quarters of Brooklyn Engine 269, first organized in 1908. Like other early twentieth-century buildings, this fire station is making the transition toward simpler lines and more restrained ornament.

HELP ONE ANOTHER
FAIR PLAY FIRE CO. No1

Left: The bell tower of the Fair Play Fire Department in Madison, Indiana, dominates this block, although the overall design of exposed brick and arched windows complement the neighboring buildings. The company's masot—known as "Little Jimmy"—serves as a weather vane.

tury, architects of firehouses embraced a "back to basics" approach, influenced not only by Prairie style but also by the red brick of firehouses from the post–Civil War era. By the end of World War I, the ornate Victorian castles and palaces had gone out of style. Wright's designs spoke of a new modernism that would be the template for nearly all future government buildings.

This new styling also reflected a change in the role of the firehouse, which was no longer seen by local governments as a city centerpiece. Instead, the firehouse was integrated into every neighborhood, and needed to blend with the prevailing residential design.

Architect Cyrus D. McLane produced a simple Prairie-style firehouse for the Rock Island, Illinois, Fire Department in 1917. It was constructed of brick with stone trim, and had a roof of composition shingle over a wood cornice. The floor was reinforced concrete, the walls plaster, and the ceiling constructed of metal. Two years earlier, architect John D. Brennan of Pittsburgh employed a similar design for Pittsburgh's Engine 61. This conservative styling did possess one radical feature: an apparatus room built for motorized fire engines only. Horses had already been phased out at this station a good five years before most other fire departments followed suit.

The gradual phase-out of the horse and the introduction of motorized fire engines spurred architects to approach the design of firehouses in a new and exciting way. While new fire engines, especially hook-and-ladder trucks, took considerable space to house, for the first time architects didn't have to consider stables and haylofts in their designs. Many firehouses were reduced to a single story, eliminating the fire pole. By 1920, firehouses were wired for electricity, and kitchens were gaining widespread popularity. Firefighting technology improved and scientific firefighting techniques emerged—a good thing, as major factories routinely employed chemicals, forcing

Below: A chemical engine sits outside its station in New York City. The firehouse abuts a commercial building, typical of the close quarters firehouses shared in burgeoning cities. Twentieth-century firefighters would have to adapt to a growing population.

fire departments to consider revolutionary approaches to fight new and more dangerous types of blazes.

Outside the firefighting community, the world was changing at breakneck speed. World War I fostered an urgent drive toward the advancement of science. The great influenza epidemic of 1918 brought radical changes in medicine. The burgeoning motion-picture industry established a toehold as an economic force in the country. Radio was invented and almost instantly became a popular new media. Professional baseball, skyscrapers, flappers, bawdy tabloid journalism, and the Jazz Age signaled a modernism that pushed aside quaint Victorian values in favor of an urgent modern world. Products were no longer designed simply to be functional, but were expected to possess characteristics appealing to consumers. Radios, telephones, toys, aircraft, and especially automobiles conveyed panache, with clean, flowing lines and smooth textures.

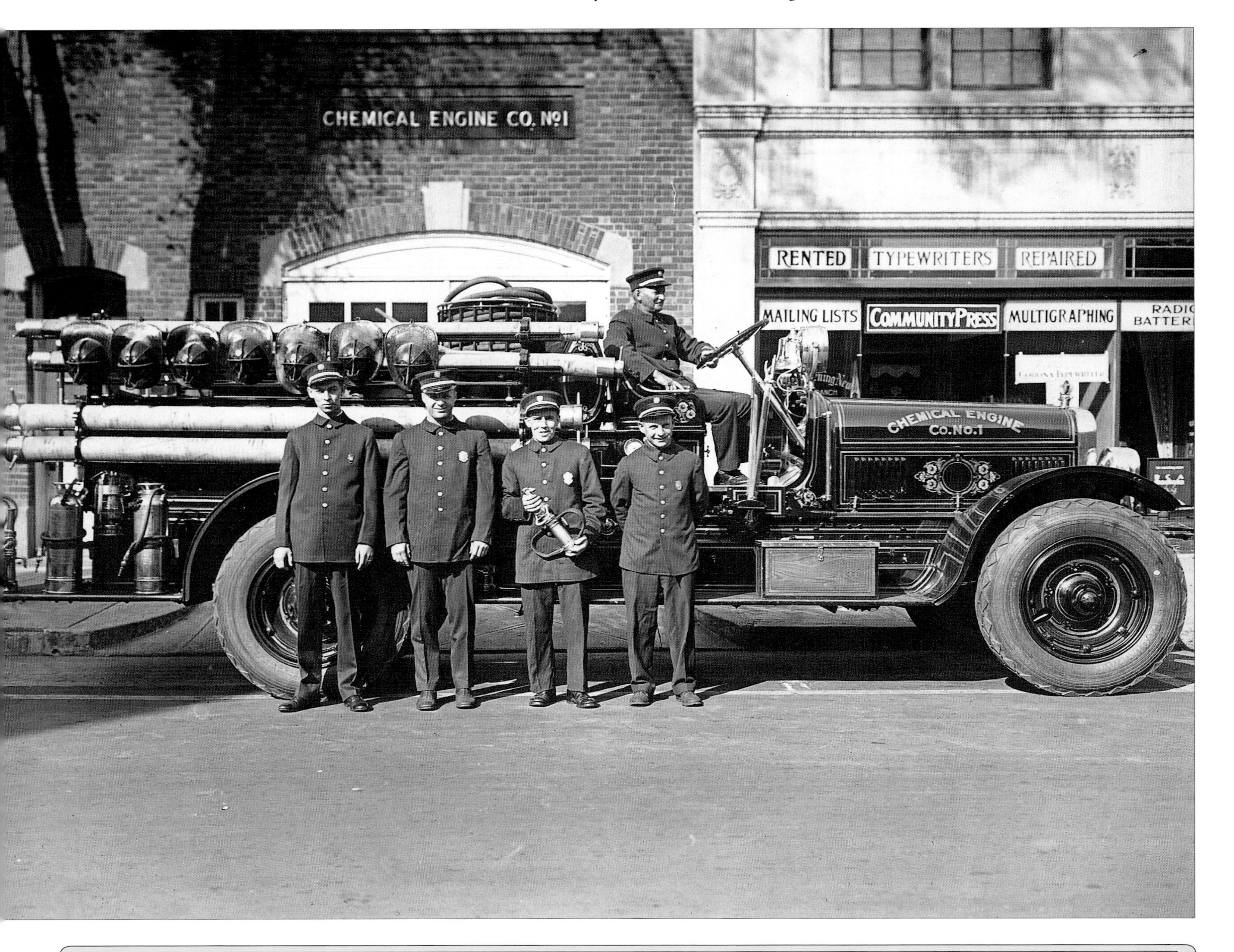

Above: A modern sensibility is reflected in this fire department building, where simple, horizontal lines lend it an efficient quality but little charm. Some subtle art deco elements mitigate the stolid pragmatism.

Architects, too, were infected with the zeal of the modern world and attempted daring new designs for both residential and commercial buildings. Thesse designs rejected longstanding architecteral traditions, turning to new shapes, materials, and uses of space. Two styles that emerged were Art Deco and Modernism, perhaps the most popular and enduring architectural styles of the twentieth century.

An eclectic design style, Art Deco developed between the two world wars. The term *Art Deco* originated from the 1925 Exposition Internationale des Arts Décoratifs Industriels et Modernes held in Paris. While Art Deco was a common design during the 1920s and '30s, it was basically a modernization of many styles, drawing on motifs from the Far and Middle East as well as on Greek and Roman themes. The hallmark of Art Deco is its use of geometry and simple shapes combined with extravagant colors. It employs touches of industrial design with a celebration of commerce and technology.

Right: Shed style became popular for residential architecture in the early 1960s, and some fire stations, especially those located in residential neighborhoods, followed the trend. This example, in Briar Cliff Manor, New York, possesses shed roofs at different heights, giving the impression of two distinct shapes bonded together.

New York City was the hub of the breathtaking Art Deco style. Construction of commercial buildings was especially heavy there during the 1920s and '30s, due to the building boom that followed WW I. This heavy rate of construction established a trend for the rest of the country. The Public Works Administration (1933–41) under Franklin D. Roosevelt cemented this modernism that still exists today.

At the height of the Art Deco movement, the Fort Worth, Texas, Fire Department adopted the style for its design of Station No. 2 at 1000 Cherry Street. Designed in 1930 by architect Herman Paul Koeppe of Wyatt C. Hedrick's firm, the station is actually two separate and distinct buildings constructed of ornate brick. The central fire station is adjoined by the fire alarm signal station. Executed in a Zigzag Moderne design, the station prominently features a 70-foot (21.3m) siren tower at the rear.

In rural areas, fire departments remained relatively conservative in approving modernistic designs, but city officials in urban settings were more willing to take chances. A year after the Fort Worth station was built, Seattle went further afield with a modernistic look that carried many elements of the Art Deco style. Fire Station No. 6, designed by architect George Stewart in 1931, is trimmed in lightning-bolt ornamentation that is perhaps more suitable for a radio station. But its theme did embrace the new philosophy of firefighting as a technological profession.

Architect James Treacy didn't go out on a limb like Seattle did when he produced designs for Engine 34 in New York City in 1931, but he did incorporate Art Deco details. This firehouse is a standard two-story affair sandwiched between two office buildings; Treacy focused on geometric forms that linked the firehouse to surrounding commercial structures. But the two large bay doors are framed in bold vertical lines etched in concrete, a simple touch that gives the structure unmistakable style.

During the same year, architect Robin Walker sketched a design for Fire Station No. 11 in Kansas City,

Missouri. Constructed of stone and mortar, it featured Art Deco flourishes but also a modest tower.

Toward the end of the Art Deco era, the city of Los Angeles chose a Streamline Moderne design for its Engine Company No. 1 in Lincoln Heights. The two-story firehouse on Pasadena Avenue faces the street and features a horizontal row of windows and an entrance door, which together form an upside down L-shape. Horizontal fins are placed above the front door, and lettering above the bay doors is treated as a horizontal line.

The Art Deco period disappeared with the onset of World War II, although many of its influences remain today. But as the need to improve the firefighting equipment and technology inside the station became a priority, exterior design became a secondary concern. As more energy was put into technology, as well as into improving living quarters, the unique styling of exteriors was lost. After the war, returning servicemen made their homes not in the city but in the ever-growing suburbs, and fire stations began to conform to suburban settings. Brick and mortar remained popular but stucco also gained wide acceptance. Structures were often built as one-story stations with flat roofs. Function replaced style, making for a more efficient fire department but also sacrificing much of the romanticism of the firefighter.

Below: This firehouse was built in 1953, once modernism had become the dominant style for public buildings. Broadly utilitarian in design, the light horizontal lines above the second-story windows display a decorative flair. The firehouse was demolished in 1989 to make way for a high-rise.

HOUS
FORD
WHITE
STAMFORD
E8

CHESHIRE
CHESHIRE
CHESHIRE

NORWICH

Previous: The Stamford, Connecticut, firehouse is representative of the tendency in firehouse design toward creating boxes for machines, brought about by the rush of new technology in the field.

Opposite, Top: Gleaming engines stand at the ready in the Chester, Connecticut, firehouse.

Opposite, Bottom: By the early 1950s, firehouse design had shifted fully toward utility, as the garage area of the Norwich, Connecticut, Fire Department shows.

Left: In Seattle, Washington, an engine leaves the station at night.

THE HISTORY OF AFRICAN-AMERICAN FIREFIGHTERS

Above: By 1953, when these two men were photographed, firehouses were slowly beginning to integrate.

The firefighting unit of Engine House No. 2 in Danville, Illinois, had a special bond with the neighborhood children. The men left their doors open and children—black and white—played with horseshoes, dangled from a trapeze, and shot games of billiards. Faces were washed, and stomachs were filled if someone was hungry.

Regularly, firefighter Clarence Kenner would gather the children and tell them stories of the fires he'd fought. Sitting on the floor, the kids would become wide-eyed as he told them of the 1915 Woodbury Book Store fire in which he was working 54 feet (16.5m) up a ladder when a wall collapsed. Two fellow firefighters were killed, and Kenner was thrown from the ladder inside the walls and onto the floor. His colleagues sprayed water around him until he could be rescued. But Kenner told the children that he was never afraid. At his feet was a portrait of Jesus Christ leaning against the wall. This picture gave him strength until his rescuers arrived.

The firehouse as a community center, perhaps even a recreation center for young children, was not unusual in prewar America. But Danville's Engine house No. 2 was different from many in that it was one of hundreds of segregated, all-black firehouses across the country. The African-American firefighter and the emergence of the segregated firehouse are as much a part of firefighting history as steamers, horses, and the sliding brass pole. As early as 1818, the African-American community recognized that to serve their neighbors they often had to organize their own departments. That year, a group of men met to organize the African Fire Association, a fire and hose company consisting of all black men.

Unfortunately, fire organizations in some cities, like Philadelphia, were less than enthusiastic about embracing the African-American firefighter. Although the city of Philadelphia was required to grant a license to any fire association applying for use of fire plugs to fight fires, white fire organizations complained that the new black regiment would actually threaten public safety. They urged city officials to deny the new association access to fire plugs. The African Fire Association immediately withdrew its application, fearing that they would further antagonize white firefighters.

But other cities, like Savannah, Georgia, permitted some African-American organizations, paying them handsomely and allowing them to wear badges, which accorded them high status in their neighborhoods. Savannah in the early 1800s permitted "free men of color, free Negroes and hired slaves" to be part of the Savannah Fire Company. Free blacks, slaves, and white supervisors worked in concert to serve the city. At one point, the company consisted of two London-built suction and discharging engines, four similar engines from New York, nearly 2,000 feet (610m) of hose, a hose cart, fifteen fire hooks, forty-four ladders, and twenty-two axes. Personnel consisted of 178 slaves, ninety-six free black men, and seventeen white men. Later, a brick firehouse was built in the northern part of Oglethorpe Ward. The company enjoyed tremendous prestige and popularity for more than twenty-five years.

By the 1840s, however, white residents had become interested in forming their own companies, including the Oglethorpe Fire Company, the Washington Fire Company, and the Young America Fire Company. Tension mounted and members of the all-white America Fire Company began to harass their black counterparts at fires, driving them away from their posts. When the city council in 1854 gave the America Fire Company control of the city's engine, Savannah members protested, but to no avail. They disbanded in November 1853. For a brief period, African-American firefighters enjoyed relative equality. In Columbia, South Carolina, for example, black and white companies, though segregated, often fought fires side by side and generally got along well.

Firefighter tournaments, immensely popular in the nineteenth century, included blacks and whites participating side by side in foot races, reel contests, and fire engine races, although no black companies were permitted to compete directly with white companies. Black firefighting tournaments often drew thousands of spectators—black and white—and fostered, at least for the day, some good will. Before and immediately following the Civil War, African-American firefighters enjoyed a civil—though unequal—relationship with their white colleagues. Soon after, however, events in the South and elsewhere moved fire departments to segregate fire companies completely. The mass lynching of blacks in the South starting in the 1880s and renewed, vigorous Ku Klux Klan

activity in the 1920s conspired to keep black men out of white firehouses for decades.

When firehouses did integrate, the directive didn't come from city fire department management. The U S Supreme Court ruling in 1954 on Brown v. Board of Education of Topeka Kansas, to abolish segregation in public schools provided the impetus. Although the ruling didn't ban segregation in other public areas, it had a tremendous effect on firehouses, and segregated firehouses began to fall like dominoes.

Still, some departments were slower than others to adopt new ways. The Los Angeles Fire Department typified the slow, lurching move toward full integration. Brown v. Board of Education was a watershed moment for integration, but to get the LAFD to open its firehouse doors to African-Americans, the National Association for the Advancement of Colored People (NAACP) had to give the department a kick-start with a series of complaints of discrimination. The campaign started in late 1953, but it wasn't until early 1956 that firefighters from all-black stations 14 and 30 on Central Avenue were fully integrated into other stations.

Until that moment, however, the department suffered a series of stops and starts by moving some African-Americans into all-white stations. Their white colleagues organized to target blacks with a "cold shoulder" treatment. Some white firefighters were even disciplined or transferred for refusing to participate in the cold shoulder treatment. Other blacks were hazed, including one African-American who had firecrackers ignited near his bunk while he was sleeping.

Other cities were even slower in integrating their fire departments. The Omaha (Nebraska) Fire Department didn't integrate its ranks until 1957, although in 1940 it moved one African-American to the department's Bureau of Fire Prevention and Inspection. Full integration in Danville, Illinios, didn't come until 1963.

It was a painful process for African-Americans, but they eventually garnered full integration and respect, becoming a fundamental part of firefighting history.

Above: In this 1943 photograph, a fireman cleans the front of an engine at Station No. 4, a segregated firehouse in Washington, D.C.
Left: Members of an African-American firehouse pose in Pittsburgh, Pennsylvania, in 1947. Note that the captain supervising this segregated engine company is white.

FIRE DEPARTMENT
820

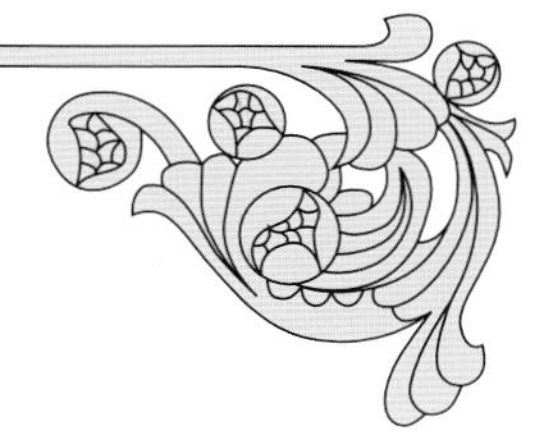

Honoring the Past

When Torrent Three was threatened by the wrecking ball in Peabody, Massachusetts, in 1988, the local historical society jumped into action to save the 1875 firehouse. The station had served the community until it closed in 1986. It remained vacant for two years, then fell into disrepair. It seemed ready for demolition.

Previous: Many old firehouses have found new life as restaurants, homes, or community buildings. Firehouse No. 3, in Elgin, Illinois, is preserved as an office building.

Below: The refurbishing of Fire Station No. 21 in St. Paul, Minnesota, was done without the original blueprints. When it was occupied by firefighters, this living and dining space may well have served as both lounge and sleeping area for the main fire company.

But historical society members and volunteers saw the Engine 3 Firehouse as a source of pride for the community of 50,000 and its 107-person fire department. Literally taking one piece of wood at time and carefully labeling it, volunteers dismantled the two-story structure and carted it away from the center of town to a barn. Eight years later, the firehouse was painstakingly re-created to its original specifications. Even its unique bell tower was rebuilt on the ground and then hoisted to its perch atop a gabled roof by, appropriately enough, the Peabody Fire Department. Rechristened the Peabody Historical Fire Museum, the firehouse now stands at the Felton-Smith historic site at Brooksby, one of the earliest settlements of Peabody.

This lengthy renovation project was conducted mainly by amateurs, with general contractors doing the electrical and heating work and a local architect offering occasional consultations. The ground floor, which originally housed the department's horse-drawn apparatus, now functions as the main museum, with a rear room also used as a display area. The second floor originally consisted of a dormitory at the front and hayloft in the rear. The sleeping quarters have been transformed into a function room, and the old hayloft is now a kitchen. The sliding pole has also been refurbished.

The Peabody firehouse is one of scores of projects across the country designed to save vintage firehouses from destruction. Many are renovated into fire museums,

and many more serve as office space or residences. Some are funded by municipal bonds approved by local voters. Others, like the Peabody project, are financed through private donations and fundraisers.

While the Peabody restoration went fairly smoothly, other amateur restorations encounter many difficulties along the way. In many cases, the historical data needed to restore a firehouse to its original grandeur may be lost forever, forcing restorers to guess. Mark Sauer, a boat builder, and Petronella Ytsma, a fine-arts photographer, faced such a challenge when they decided to restore and convert into a home and workshop Fire Station No. 21 at the corner of Baker and Ohio streets in St. Paul, Minnesota. Their challenge was more unique than many other firehouse restoration projects, for Station No. 21 was built in 1910 but only served as a firehouse until 1938. It then went on to become home to the American Legion and later a gymnastics club. By the time Saur and Ytsma saw the debilitated structure in 1994, it was in sad shape. And worse, not only did the St. Paul Fire Department have no photographs of the building in its archives, but the blueprints had apparently been lost.

The couple was fortunate that the exterior—red brick and mortar with a limestone foundation—was in solid shape. They replaced the existing tar and gravel roof with a membrane roof and the windows with double-hung windows, believed to have been close to the originals in spirit. Inside, the original maple hardwood floor was refurbished. When the firehouse was featured in a St. Paul home tour, old-timers pointed to an area where they believed the sliding pole was located. But Saur and Ytsma found no evidence that the second floor had been cut or patched where a pole would be found, no sign that the structure ever featured a sliding pole.

On the ground floor the interior measures 25 feet (7.6m) wide and 100 feet (30.5m) long, with a lofty 14-foot (4.3m) ceiling; the second floor features 11-foot (3.4m) ceilings. The building is flanked by two turrets, one that contains its original wrought-iron staircase and another that was used for drying fire hoses. Downstairs, most of the floor space is taken up by Saur's boat-building work, but the 10-foot-wide (3m) bay doors—once able to accommodate horse-drawn apparatus and vintage 1930s motorized fire engines—limit the size of boats he can bring inside. To the rear of the structure, where the firehouse's offices were originally located, is Ytsma's photography studio.

The second floor features living quarters in the east end of the building with two bedrooms—where the fire captain and lieutenant once had separate sleeping quarters—and one huge room that serves as a living and dining room. A primary wall divides the kitchen area, which was once the building's hayloft. At the west end of the building is office space. During a previous renovation in

Left: The turret in the foreground at Fire Station No. 21 was once used to dry fire hoses.

Above: Cities with shifting, growing populations were often less concerned with preserving their older buildings, which were frequently razed to make way for new construction.

the 1960s, dark wood paneling and fluorescent lights had been installed, but were removed under the couple's restoration.

In Station No. 21's case, the integrity of the building's exterior remains intact, along with vital components of the interior, such as the wrought-iron staircase and hardwood floors. It's an excellent example of a restoration successfully completed despite the absence of archival photographs and blueprints.

ARCHITECTURAL INVESTIGATIONS

Major restorations, particularly those involving designated historical landmarks and those funded by municipal bond money, require intense investigation by architectural firms that specialize in historic rehabilitation. Brick and wood-frame buildings are most common in North America, but determining a firehouse's, history requires

Left: A building present on the lot when the city of Richmond, Virginia, bought it in 1849 became Steamer Co. No. 5; the firehouse was renovated in 1883 and 1898, bringing the original structure to its current condition. When the station was threatened with demolition in the late 1970s, a local citizen whose father and grandfather had served with Steamer Co. No. 5 rescued the building, which now serves as the Virginia Fire and Police Museum.

Below: Some firehouses have not been lucky enough to benefit from preservation efforts. The quarters of Engine Co. 44 of South Boston (here shown with its fireboat) were abandoned in 1948.

Following pages: After the Civil War, firehouses were built with brick and designed for more utilitarian uses. Here, firefighters display an aerial ladder truck.

Below: Built by the McSheehy Brothers in 1909, this Mission Revival structure housed San Francisco's Chemical Engine No. 44. Auctioned in 1959, it is now a home and artist's studio.

Right: This typical two-story wooden firehouse in Colorado was built in 1899 for the Goldfield Fire Department.

Opposite: The 1894 Aurora, Illinois, Fire Department was designed with Victorian elements and topped by an onion dome. Now the building is home to the Aurora Regional Fire Museum.

an investigator's expertise. By understanding the building's history and the quality of its workmanship, restorers can judge whether a building can be saved, and if so, the extent and cost-effectiveness of the renovation.

Architectural investigators often start by examining the brickwork, which provides vital information about the construction of a building. The color, size, shape, and texture of the brick provide clues to whether the material was hand-molded and traditionally fired in a clamp with hardwoods, or whether it was machine-molded and fired in a kiln, a more modern technique. This information helps investigators understand when the building was constructed and where the materials were produced, and perhaps even whether structural elements were repaired or replaced at a later time. Masonry mortar can likewise reveal whether it was produced in a traditional or modern manner.

Wood, on the other hand, presents an entirely different set of challenges. Investigators must determine whether the wood was cut by an ax, pit saw, mill saw, or band saw, all of which indicate a time period of construction. By studying the wood's surfaces, investigators can also tell if it was gouged, carved, or planed by hand. Roofs are more difficult to examine for time and place of construction because, since they are exposed to the elements and are rarely regularly maintained (as a building's exterior may be) they generally last no longer than fifty years before being replaced.

If documents are missing, investigators may rely on the structure itself to pinpoint its construction period, but they must be careful not to be fooled by architectural details. Design and stylistic periods are fairly broad and are subject to many regional variations. Thus, they are not reliable tools for identifying the date of construction. For example, one might consider Richardsonian Romanesque

A
F
D

FIRST
BAPTIST
CHAPEL

Opposite, Top: Lit up at night, Reily Fire Station No. 10, now a fire museum, was once a reassuring site to the Harrisburg, Pennsylvania, community.

Opposite, Bottom: This survivor of the 1906 San Francisco earthquake, with its exposed brick painted white and its windows replaced by steel bars, has served a number of uses in its time. Originally built in 1886 as a storehouse for the fire department's apparatus and supplies, the structure later became a stable for department horses and then home to Engine Co. No. 27. After passing out of SFFD hands, it was home to the First Baptist Church before becoming a private school. A pediment above the main door is still emblazoned with S.F.F.D.

Left: Fireman's Hall preserves antique fire pieces in Philadelphia. Such displays are fitting reminders of the gradual advances in technology made over the long history of firefighting.

Right: This firehouse—in Boston's Charlestown—was remodeled in 1918 for motorized fire engines. Renovations made earlier in the station's history can add to the confusion when professionals set about to restore a building. While signature architectural details may help preservationists identify the date of the building, they are no substitute for a complete history and blueprints.

Above: Equipment, too, is often collected and restored. Here, the front of a postwar Ford fire engine gleams brightly.

to have flourished only between 1870 and 1895, but some architects influenced by this style may have employed elements of the Romanesque style long after it had generally lost favor. A building's design may provide some clues, however. For example, certain decorative flourishes on a building may indicate a transition between styles or provide a clue to an original style that was upgraded through new work.

Generally, the process of architectural investigation includes a reconnaissance of all of these elements, including "surface mapping" the building, a process that demands a detailed look at all exterior and interior surfaces. In surface mapping, every detail of the design and construction of a building is examined and, often, documentary drawings and photographs record or map the evidence. The investigation includes nondestructive testing, which is designed to provide information with little or no damage to the historic fabric of the building. Among the nondestructive tests performed are X-rays, which reveal nail types and joining; inserting mirrors into tight spaces to view the construction; and even use of fiber-optic lenses and ultraviolet or infrared light to observe actual materials and finishes. Small samples of wood, mortar, brick, paint, and plaster are taken to determine the age and quality of the building. As a last resort, if the evidence gathered under these methods is inconclusive, "destructive testing" is performed. This involves removing—and therefore destroying to some degree—some historic fabric to gather vital information. For example, a portion of a floor or wall may be removed for close examination. Depending on the type of renovation, the building's needs, the project's budget, and the organization conducting the renovation, the architectural investigation may be minimal or very intensive.

Right: Common in upstate New York, Colonial Revival architecture is seen at the Mombasha Firehouse in Monroe.

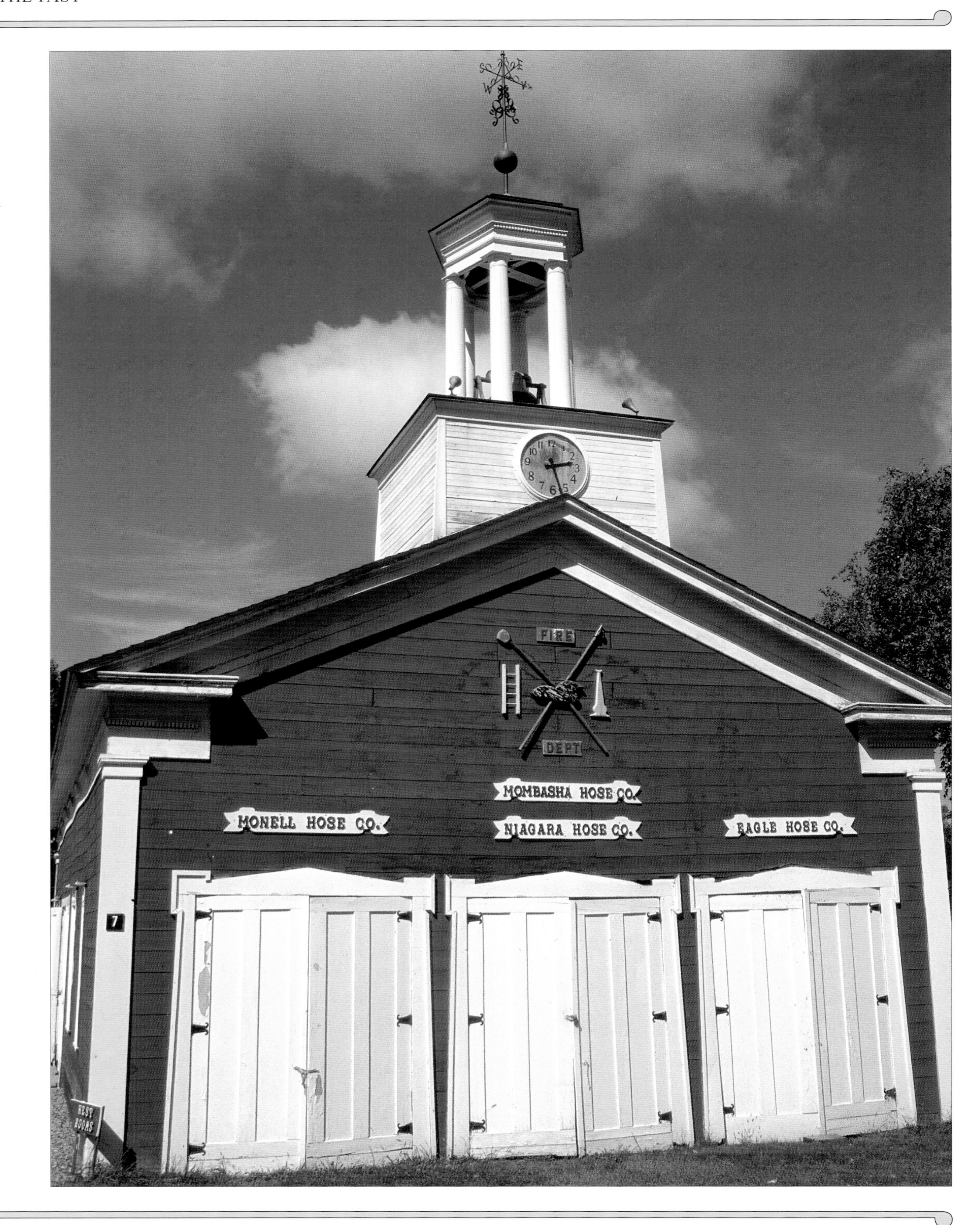

VINTAGE FIREHOUSES RESTORED

All across North America, community leaders are recognizing the beauty of the buildings that for so long were dedicated to preserving the survival of the neighborhood. Rather than tearing these historic buildings down, they are working to find new, creative uses for the space, uses that allow developers to renovate the buildings and preserve the building's legacy of providing useful service to the community. The following stories tell of successful renovations that celebrate the heritage and the enduring quality of these magnificent structures.

The Presidio Fire Station

In San Francisco, Presidio Trust architect Chandler McCoy was faced with a firehouse built in 1917 that had undergone a series of external and internal changes over more than eight decades. Now a designated historical landmark, the Presidio Fire Station was built following a fire that took the lives of the wife and three daughters of Brigadier General John J. "Black Jack" Pershing, who was away fighting Pancho Villa in Mexico. The uproar over the slow response of the San Francisco Fire Department prompted the U S Government to build its own station on the Presidio. It was the first military fire department to be established and then staffed by a civilian fire crew.

Below: A simple buckboard, probably once belonging to the fire chief, is on display at the San Francisco City Hall. More than most, this city has done much to preserve its firefighting past.

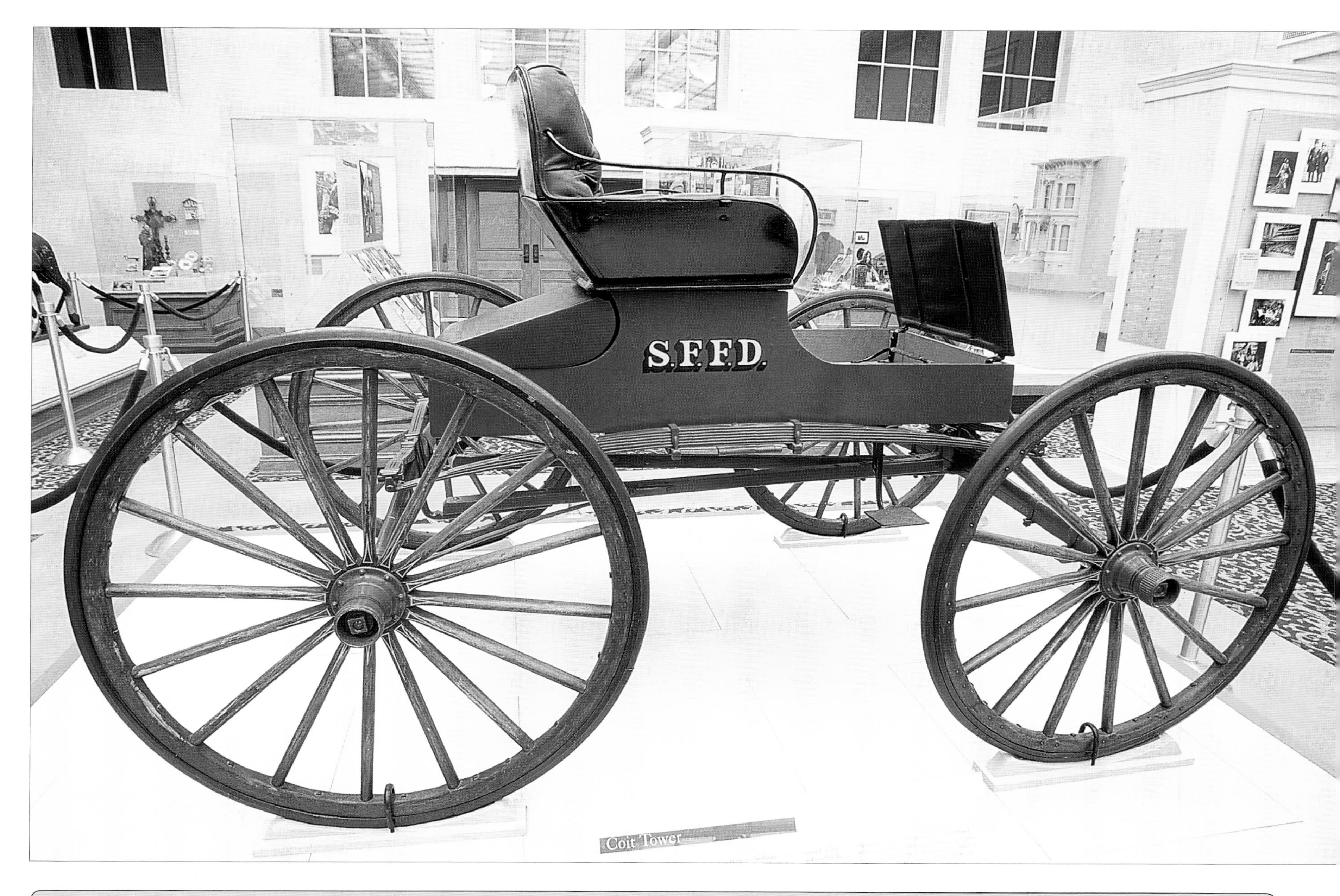

Below: This Louis Maurer painting, titled "The American Fireman, Always Ready," testifies to our long-standing admiration for firefighters.

Although many fire departments across the country were still using horses in 1917, the government chose to design its firehouse for motorized apparatus. Wood-frame finished with stucco, and in a lapwood style, the two-story building also featured a hose tower.

In the 1990s there was considerable controversy as to whether the building should be demolished and a new, state-of-the-art facility constructed to replace it. But local firefighters and government officials decided that it was important to keep the fire department operating on the site it had used for more than eighty years. McCoy and other architects and contractors were faced with the task of adhering to historical preservation requirements while at the same time bringing the structure up to current building codes. The most daunting task was to retrofit the building to meet current seismic codes; then space for newer and larger equipment needed to be added, all while managing to maintain the building's historic stature. In many ways, the structure is a fairly straightforward building, as conservative in design as most military structures. Yet in large part, it is a distinctive and attractive affair, made of stucco with unusual projecting bay window dormers at the front. And in terms of proportion, the structure's composition is elegant.

Performing a thorough architectural investigation, McCoy, employed as the project manager for the Presidio Trust (which administers the Presidio), had access to volumes of military photographs that chronicled the life span of the firehouse from its birth through its myriad changes over the decades. He also had original blueprints to work from. Unlike Fire Station No. 21 in St. Paul, Minnesota, McCoy was fortunate to have an intimate knowledge of the building.

With the stated goal of restoring the building to its original appearance, McCoy wrote a set of guidelines for architects and contractors to work from. Modern offices were established in the old open garage space, and additional garage facilities were built to closely match the original design of the building. A receptionist area and a front door that hadn't existed previously were created to provide easy entry and a space for visitors

to the building to be screened and announced. The kitchen added in the 1930s was removed, and a parking lot that had been installed at the same time was reconfigured. Although McCoy could never substantiate the long-held myth that the firehouse was built using housing material from the World's Fair of 1915 in San Francisco, the story adds to the allure of the restored structure. The completed restoration was awarded the prestigious California Preservation Foundation design award.

The Pawtucket Firehouse

Pawtucket, Rhode Island, also committed itself to preserving a historic firehouse, but it had a different set of obstacles to conquer. The two-story Queen Anne–style brick firehouse, originally built in 1887–88, was used as a

Above: A steam engine, once the workhorse of the Seattle, Washington, Fire Department, is now a museum piece.

P. B. F.
ENGINE Co. No. 42

42

Previous: A firefighting crew poses outside an urban firehouse constructed in 1895 and designed more for horse-drawn apparatus than for the motorized kind. Note the snow chains on the rear wheels.

Right: Overcoats and helmets must stand at the ready for the sound of the alarm.

fire station from 1890 to 1974. After its retirement, several city agencies occupied the space.

The building, both exterior and interior, is exceptionally attractive, and its proximity to highways in Rhode Island and Massachusetts made it a natural choice for office space. The interior was modernized and restored in 1982, but it retained its charming miscellany of nooks and crannies. The 52-foot (15.8m) hose-drying tower was transformed into a bell tower, and a spiral stairway and large vertical windows with heavy wooden moldings in the front were rehabilitated. The building's sturdy construction and prime location made it much sought after by developers. In 1982, one developer wanted to convert the firehouse into a restaurant with offices above, while another advanced a plan for an offices-only renovation. A third developer hoped to convert the vintage firehouse into a two-story restaurant. Steep restoration costs and controversies surrounding the issuance of liquor licenses held up the final determination of the project. Several developers came and went.

Meanwhile, the building became eligible for nomination to the National Register of Historic Landmarks, which would further complicate the restoration process by limiting how and for what reason a restoration was performed. The project then suffered another series of setbacks when it was hit by several arson fires. The building literally saved itself because its structural supports of twelve-inch (30cm) thick diagonal beams smoldered during the fire, but did not burn. Amazingly, the structure still met safety codes. Extensive interior renovations were performed, but the exterior—due to the requirements of the National Register of Historic Places—remained intact and was returned to its original splendor. Following renovations, the firehouse reopened as an office building, proud home to an environmental assessment, engineering, and remediation company.

The Trenton Central Fire Headquarters

When local officials decided to restore the 1927 Trenton Central Fire Headquarters in Trenton, New Jersey, the architectural firm of Venturi, Scott Brown and Associates, Inc., was commissioned. The 54,386-square-foot (16,577sqm) Renaissance palazzo–style firehouse accommodated administrative operations, a fire museum, and support spaces.

The three-story building was originally constructed to be "fire-proof," with virtually all the components made of metal and concrete. Only the handrails on the staircase were made of wood. The exterior is a combination of granite and red brick, with the front French windows on the second floor opening on to a false balcony. The high bifold doors to the garage on the first floor had long since been replaced with aluminum doors, but aluminum bifold doors were installed to help retain the building's original character. An addition, designed to match the original firehouse, was also constructed; it houses apparatus and service bays and workshops.

Firemen's Hall

In the village of Tivoli in New York, there was no doubt what villagers wanted to do with its Firemen's Hall when it was retired from active duty in 1986. The architectural firm of Mendel, Mesick, Cohen, Waite & Hall was chosen to conduct an architectural investigation to determine whether it was feasible to restore the firehouse. Restoration would be financed through grants from the Duchess County Arts Council and from the New York State Council of the Arts, as well as through private donations. The town was fortunate that it had a relatively perfect historical specimen.

The Tivoli Firemen's Hall owed its existence to the frustration of town leader John Watts de Peyster, a feisty, mercurial man who was disgusted with the behavior of local volunteer firefighters. De Peyster considered himself a student of firefighting technology and had even been a volunteer firefighter while attending Columbia College. He developed strong opinions about firefighting and didn't appreciate the freewheeling nature of the late-nineteenth-century firefighter. He became an avid proponent of the professional fire department.

"The scenes I have witnessed, in this service of wanton destruction, unnecessary flooding, frolicking, fighting and bullying, would fill a good many pages, but tend to no good," de Peyster once wrote. "The volunteer fire department lasted a great deal longer than it should have been tolerated."

De Peyster built his country residence at Tivoli after his marriage in 1841 to Estelle Livingston. He traveled widely and studied the firefighting techniques of Europeans before returning home. Meanwhile, he donated countless public monuments, churches, schools, and libraries to surrounding communities. By 1890, Tivoli had grown to 1,350 residents and was in desperate need of a firehouse.

In 1898, de Peyster commissioned architect Michael O'Conner of Hudson, New York, to build Firemen's Hall. O'Conner chose a Richardsonian Romanesque design, although the style was considered somewhat dated in some architectural circles; O'Conner's plan featured a "storefront" façade, which was popular during that era.

The three-story building is brick laid in English bond. The façade is horizontally divided with contrasting stone coursing at the floor levels, setting off the doors and fenestration from the brickwork. The building is capped by a hipped Pennsylvania gray slate roof, punctuated by a dormer and a pair of tall heavy chimneys on the east and west elevations. The southwest corner of the roof gives rise to a tower capped by a round turreted cupola—the tower housed the fire alarm and also served to dry the hoses. Flourishes include a stone course with oak-leaf-patterned blocks along its length, which allude to the tra-

Below: Long before there were sirens, or even whistles, there were bells to sound the alarm as prewar fire engines raced to a blaze.

Opposite: A Dalmatian has a little fun with the firehouse cat.

ditional European use of heraldic symbols (the oak leaf is the time-honored European emblem for firefighters).

O'Conner, who designed his own home in the Queen Anne style, adhered to a conservative interpretation of Romanesque design with modest touches and stone accents. He kept ornamentation at the street level, mainly at the doorway, and the cornice line, with detail that led the eye upward. The magnificence of the building stood out among its modest neighbors in this small community.

When Mendel, Mesick, Cohen, Waite & Hall conducted its investigation, it found Firemen's Hall in remarkably good condition, considering it was ninety years old. Most of its original building fabric was intact and all of its interior spaces had survived without major alterations. As was expected, the most serious problem with the building was the badly deteriorated roof. Inside, the antiquated heating, electrical, and plumbing systems were in poor shape, and the leaky roof had resulted in plaster damage to walls. But overall, the architectural firm found a rare nineteenth-century building that, for the most part, remained in its original state.

The building has been restored to its original appearance, including the entry, ramps, and doors at the front of the building. The two large rectangular garage bays, bisected by a central hallway, have been transformed into the Village Free Library and an exhibition space for antique firefighting memorabilia. On the second floor are offices for the mayor, the zoning board, the village clerk, and the village court. The third floor remains a large open space designed for meetings. The structure continues to hold a special place in the townspeople's hearts.

Today, our historic firehouses continue to serve their communities, whether restored for new use as a modern fire station or preserved in the form of a museum, residence, business, or office space. Solid construction and investigative techniques used by architectural firms have made such restorations possible. But the real force behind these restoration efforts remains the community and their desire to preserve their heritage.

Fire Museums

Following is an extensive listing of fire museums, many of which are housed in vintage fire stations.

UNITED STATES

Alabama

Phoenix Fire Museum
P.O. Box 2068
Mobile, AL 33302
(334) 208-7569

Arizona

Hall of Flame
6101 E. Van Buren Street
Phoenix, AZ 85008
(602) 275-3473

California

African-American Firefighter Museum
1401 South Central Avenue
Los Angeles, CA 90021
(213) 744-1730

Ahrens-Fox Fire Buffs' Association
Senter Rd. & Quin Ave, San Jose, CA
1220 Tasman Drive #133
Sunnyvale, CA 94089 (mailing address)
(408) 279-2423 or
(408) 734-1902

Benicia Fire Museum
P.O. Box 1251
Benecia, CA 94510
(707) 745-1688

California Fire & Safety Museum
1867 Ellard Place
Concord, CA 94521
(510) 687-6426

County of Los Angeles Fire Museum
LA County Fire Department HQ
1320 N. Eastern Avenue
Los Angeles, CA 90063

Fire Service Museum & Home & Fire Safety Ctr.
Orange Co. Fireman's Association
34681 Calle Fortuna
Capistrano Beach, CA 92624
(714) 581-1910

Glendale Fire Department Museum
Fire Station 21
421 Oak Strees
Glendale , CA
(818)548-4810

Long Beach Firefighters Museum
1445 Peterson Street
Long Beach, CA 90813
(562) 570-2985
e-mail: LBFDMuseum@hotmail.com

Los Angeles Fire Department Museum and Memorial
LAFD Historical Society
2900 West Temple St.
Los Angeles, CA. 90028
(213) 380-2900 xt 290

Napa Fire Museum
Napa City Firefighters Association
1201 Main Street
Napa, CA 94559
(707) 259-0609

Old Plaza Firehouse
134 Plaza Street
Los Angeles, CA 90012
(213) 625-3741

Old West Fire Museum
1470 Rose Street
Berkeley, CA 94702
(510) 524-4969

Pioneer Fire Company Museum
247 S. Boyd Street No. A
San Bernadino, CA
(909) 885-6280

San Diego Firehouse Museum
1572 Columbia Street
San Diego, CA 92101
(619) 232-3473

.San Francisco Fire Dept. Museum
St. Francis Hook & Ladder Society
655 Presidio Avenue
P.O. Box 26383
San Francisco, CA 94102
(414) 558-3546

Colorado

Alma Firehouse Museum
P.O. Box 336
Alma, CO 70420-336
(719) 836-2803

Antique Firehouse
3312 North Garfield Avenue
Loveland, CO 80537
(303) 667-7040

Denver Firefighters Museum
1326 Tremont Place
Denver, CO 80204
(303) 892-1436

Fire Museum No. 3
2160"B"Street
Colorado Springs, CO 80906
(719) 576-1200

Hose Company No. 3
Colorado Fire Buffs Historical Soc.
116 Broadway
P.O. Box 4127
Pueblo, CO 81004
(719) 544-4548

Old Station No. 15
1080 Clayton Street
Denver, CO 80206
(303) 377-7445

Poudre Fire Authority
102 Remington
Fort Collins, CO 80524
(303) 221-6581

Red, White, and Blue Fire Company
P.O. Box 8135
Breckenridge, CO 80424
(303) 453-1509

Connecticut

Bethel Historical Fire Fighting Museum
36 South Street
Bethel, CT 06801
(203) 743-3825

Cannon Square Fire Dept. and Museum
270 N. Water Street
Cannon Square, CT 06378-9704
(203) 535-3471

Connecticut Fire Museum
58 North Road
P.O. Box 297
East Windsor, CT 06088-0297
(860) 623-4732

The Fire Museum
Conn. Firemen's Historical Society
230 Pine Street
Manchester, CT 06040
(860) 649-9436

N.W. Conn. Firefighting Museum of Torrington
P.O. Box 1041
Torrington, CT 06790

Above: Firefighter museums across the country take loving care to recreate firehouses as th
California have re-established a nineteenth century barn that houses wagons and a chemic

Delaware

Christiana Fire Company Museum
2 East Main Street
Christiana, DE 19702

Wilmington Fire Dept. Museum
300 North Walnut Street
Wilmington, DE 19801

Florida

Jacksonville Fire Museum
107 Market Street
Jacksonville, FL 32202
(904) 633-3473

National Kid's Fire Museum
13094 95th Street, North
Largo, FL 34643
(813) 585-5360

Orange County Historical Society
Fire Station 3 Museum
812 East Rollins Street
Orlando, FL 32803
(407) 897-6350

Pompano Beach Fire Museum
P.O. Box 154
Pompano Beach, FL 33061
(305) 786-4348

Georgia

Clune Fire Museum
1885 Windsor Wood Drive
Rosewell, GA 30075
(404) 594-9150

Firehouse/Museum
Martin Luther King Nat'l Historic Site
National Park Service
Atlanta, GA

Marietta Fire Station 1 Museum
112 Haynes Street
Marietta, GA 30060
(770) 528-0723

Roswell Fire Museum
1002 Alpharetta Street
Roswell, GA 30075
(404) 641-3730

Woodbine International Fire Museum
100 Bedell Avenue
P.O. Box 58
Woodbine, GA 31569-0058
(912) 576-5351

Idaho

Idaho Forest Fire Museum
Moscow, ID
(208) 882 4767

Illinois

Aurora Regional Fire Museum
53 N. Broadway Rt. 25
P.O. Box 1782
Aurora, IL 60507
(708) 892-1572

Chicago Area Fire Museum
1001 N. Main Street
Wauconda, IL 60084

Elgin Fire Barn No. 5 Museum
533 St. Charles Street
Elgin, IL 60120
(847) 697-6242

Engine House No. 2 Historical Assn.
705 N. Walnut
Danville, IL 61832
(217) 446-0363

ere, the staff at Bodie State Historic Park in

Fire Museum of Greater Chicago
1338 N. Wicker Park
Chicago, IL 60622

Granite City Fire Dept. Historical Museum
Engine House No.1
1411 19th Street
Granite City, IL 62040
(618) 931-3723

Illinois State Fire Museum
1035 Stevenson Drive
Springfield, IL 62703-4259
(217) 785-1021

Moline Fire Department Museum
1630 Eighth Avenue
Moline, IL 61265

"The Room on Fire"
David J. Traiforos
1923 74th Avenue
Elmwood Park, IL 60707

Spinello's Fire Memorabilia Museum
2126 Barton Blvd.
Rockford, IL 61103-3709
(815) 968-5693

Indiana

Conway Fire Museum
4115 Profit Court - New Albany Industrial Park N.
P.O. Box 711
New Albany, IN 47151
(812) 945-2617

Fire Museum of Indiana
794 Landersdale Road
Camby, IN 46113

Fort Wayne Firefighters Museum Inc.
226 West Washington Blvd.
P.O. Box 10404
Fort Wayne, IN 46852
(219) 426-0051

Historical Fire Station No. 9
1728 S. Eighth Street
Terre Haute, IN 47802
(818) 235-9865

Iowa

Clear Lake Fire Museum
112 North Sixth Street
Clear Lake, IA 50428

International Fire Museum
2301 E11th St.
Davenport, IA
(319) 323-7726

Kansas

Kansas Fire Museum
Wichita, KS 66109

Kentucky

Louisville FD Learning Ctr. & Museum
3228 River Park Drive
Louisville, KY 40210
(502) 574-3701

Louisiana

Baton Rouge Fire Museum
427 Laurel Street
Baton Rouge, LA 70801
(504) 344-8558

Louisiana State Fire Museum
205 Lafayette Street
Gretna, LA 70053
(504) 361-3696

New Orleans Fire Dept Museum & Edu. Center.
1135 Washington Avenue
New Orleans, LA 70130
(504) 896-4756

Shreveport Fire Fighter's Museum
601 Spring Streeet
P.O. Box 1064
Shreveport, LA 71130
(318) 222-0227

Maine

City of Portland Fire Museum
Portland Fire Buffs
P.O. Box 3161
Portland, ME 04101
(207) 929-5352

Great Harbor Collections Inc.
Old Firehouse Station
P.O. Box 145
Northeast Harbor, ME 04662

Hose No. 5 Fire Museum
247 State Street
P.O. Box 25
Bangor, ME 04401
(207) 989-5580
(207) 537-2423

Maryland

Baltimore City Fire Museum
Box 414 Association
414 N. Gay Street
Baltimore, MD 21202

Baltimore Equitable Society Fire Museum
21 N. Eutaw Street
Baltimore, MD 21201
(410) 727-1794

Cheasapeake Fire Museum
Route 670
P.O. Box 400
Hebron, MD 21830
(410) 860-0843

Fire Museum of Maryland
1301 York Road
Lutherville, MD 21093
(410) 321-7500

Fireman's Historical Foundation
200 Washington Street
Berlin, MD 21811

Massachusetts

American Hand Fire Engine Society
Zero Morgan Avenue
Newbury, MA 01951
(508) 465-3948

Atlantic No. 1
Burrill Street
Swampscott, MA 01907
(617) 592-7446

Bare Cove Fire Museum
Bare Cove Park - 19 Rear Fort Hill St.
P.O. Box 262
Hingham, MA 02043-0262
(617) 749-0028

Berkshire Co. Museum of Firefighting
669 Perks Road
Pittsfield, MA 01201
Boston Fire Museum
344 Congress Street
Boston, MA 02210
(617) 482-1344

Brockton Fire Museum
216 N. Pearl Street
Brockton, MA 02401
(508) 580-0039

Nantucket Fire Hose Cart House
8 Garden Street
Nantucket Historical Association
P.O. Box 1016
Nantucket, MA 02554
(508) 228-1894

New Bedford Fire Museum
Bedford St. & S. Sixth St.
New Bedford, MA 02740

New England Fire and History Museum
1439 Main Street
Brewster, MA 02631
(508) 896-5711

Old Fire Museum
North Main Street
South Hadley, MA 01075

Peabody Historical Fire Museum
35 Washington Street
Peabody, MA 01960
(978) 531-0805

Michigan

Engine House 11 - Detroit Fire Museum
Detroit, MI
(313) 224-2035

Engine House No. 5
6610 Lake Michigan Drive
Allendale, MI 49401
(616) 895-7550

Hackley Hose Co. 2 Fire Barn Museum
430 W. Clay Ave.
Muskegon, MI 49440
(516) 722-0278 510

Michigan Antique Fire Equipment Preservation Group
110 W. Cross St.
Ypsilanti, MI 48197
(734) 547-0663
e-mail: firemuseum@msn.com

Wolverine Fire Company
13280 Verona Road
Battle Creek, MI 49014
(616) 968-2998

Minnesota

Austin Firefighting Museum
Mower County Fairgrounds
Austin, MN 55912

Bill and Bonnie Daniels
Fire Hall & Museum
15501 Crest Drive
Burnsville, MN 55306
(952) 435-7015

Hinklye Fire Museum
Hinckley, MN 55037
(612) 384-7338

Missouri

Fire Museum of Missouri
908 East Business Route 60-63
Willow Springs, MO. 65793
(417) 469-4589
e-mail: UsFireHouse.com

595 Firehouse Museum, Memorial Garden and Fireschool
1078 S. Main St.
Springfield, MO 65807-1418
(417) 864-7655 Fax: 417-864-7917

Jefferson City Fire Museum
7115 Loesch Rd.
Jefferson City, MO 65109
(314) 496-3896

Kansas City Fire Brigade Museum
Old Fire Station 10
1019 Cherry Street
Kansas City, MO 64106
(816) 474-0200

Reliance Fire Co. Museum
5637 Cedar Ct.
Parkerville, MO 64152
(816) 741-2605
e-mail: dklink@kc.rr.com

St. Louis Fire Department Museum
1421 North Jefferson Street
St. Louis, MO 63106-2136
(314) 533-3406

Mississippi

American Heritage "Big Red" Fire Museum
650 North Church Avenue
Louisville, MS 39339
(601) 773-3421

Jackson Fire Department
555 South West Street
Jackson, MS 39201

Jackson Public Fire Safety Education and Fire Museum
355 Woodrow Wilson
Jackson, MS 39213
(601) 960-2433
(601) 960-2432 fax

Old Firehouse Museum
340 Main Street (mailing)
216 Main Street (location)
Greenville, MS, 38701
(601) 378-1538
(601) 378-1564

North Carolina

Catawba County Firefighters Museum
3957 Herman Sipes Road
Conover, NC 28613
(704) 466-0911

Kings Mountain Fire Department Historical Fire Museum
P.O. Box 429
Kings Mountain, NC 28086
(704) 734-0555

Market Fire House Museum
Old Salem District
Winston-Salem, NC 27102
(910) 721-7300

New Bern Firemen's Museum
Central Fire Station
408 Hancock Street
New Bern, NC 28560
(919) 636-4087

Oasis Wagoneers / Antique Fire Museum
Oasis Shrine Temple
Charlotte, NC 28256

Nebraska

Lincoln Fire Department Museum
Fire Station No. 1
1801 "Q" Street
Lincoln, NE 68508
(402) 471-7363

Nevada

Fire Fighters Museum of Nevada
575 E. Flamingo RD.
Las Vegas, NV. 89119
(702) 460-2604

Nevada State / Comstock Fire Museum
Liberty Engine Co. No. 1
P.O. Box 466
Virginia City, NV 89440
(702) 847-0666

Warren Engine Co. No. 1 Fire Museum
Carson City Fire Department
777 South Stewart Street
Carson City, NV 89701
(775) 887-2210

New Hampshire

Franklin Fire Fighters Museum
59 West Bow Street
Franklin, NH 03235
(603) 934-2205

Monitor Engine Co. Firehouse Museum
P.O. Box 1066
Wolfeboro, NH 03894
(603) 569-4997

New Hampshire Fire Museum
4 Patricia Court
Enfield, NH 03748
(603) 632-4998

New Jersey

Bayonne Firefighters Museum
10 West 47th Street
Bayonne, NJ 07002
(201) 858-6199

Cape May Fire Department Museum
643 Washington Street
Cape May, NJ 08204
(609) 884-9512

Dover Fire Museum
209 N. Sussex Street
Dover, NJ 07801
(201) 366-0301

Engine Company No. 5 Museum
415 N. Essex Avenue
Margate, NJ 08402

Eureka Fire Museum
39 Washington Avenue
Milltown, NJ 08850
(908) 828-0221 or (908) 828-7207

Fire District No. 3 - Old Bridge Township
39 Throck Morton Lane
Old Bridge, NJ 08857

Firefighters Museum of S. New Jersey
8 E. Ryon Avenue
Pleasantville, NJ 08232
(609) 641-9300

Friendship Fire Company Museum
29 Delaware Street
Woodbury, NJ 08096
609-845-0066

Haddon Fire Company #1 Museum
15 N. Haddon Avenue
Haddonfield, NJ 08033
(609) 429-4308

Hoboken Exempt Firemen's Assn. Museum
213 Bloomfield Street
Hoboken, NJ 07030
(201) 420-2397

Meredith Havens Fire Museum
244 Perry Street, 3rd Floor
Trenton, NJ 08618
(609) 883-1569

N. Plainfield Exempt Firemen's Assn. Museum
300 Somerset Street
Borough of North Plainfield F. D.
8 Lincoln Place
North Plainfield, NJ 07060
(908) 769-2932

New Jersey Fireman's Home Museum
565 Lathrop Avenue
Boonton, NJ 07005
(201) 334-0024

New Jersey State Fire Engine Museum
175 Washington Street
Long Branch NJ 07740
Ph: (732) 222-5783
fax: (732) 229-77908
e-mail: FireMuseumNJ@rbfd.com

Newark FD Historical Assn. Museum
49 Washington Street
Newark, NJ 07102
(201) 596-6550

Newton Fire Museum
150 Spring Street
Newton, NJ 07860
(201) 383-0396

Schierle's Fire Museum
825 Grant Avenue
Westfield, NJ 07090-2322
(201)233-3838

Somerville Exempt Firemen's Museum
North Doughty Avenue
Somerville, NJ 08876

Union Fire Co. #1 Belmar Fire Department
Ninth Ave. and E. Street
Belmar, NJ 07719-0091
(732) 280-2085
(732) 280-2085 fax

New Mexico

Wildland Firefighter Museum
111 West Smokey Bear Blvd.
Box 1304,
Capitan NM 88316
(505) 354-4251

New York

American Museum of Fire Fighting
125 Harry Howards Avenue
Hudson, NY 12534
(518) 828-7695

Brookhaven Town Volunteer Firefighters Museum
Route 25 (Middle Country Road)
Ridge, Long Island, New York 11961
(516) 924-8114

Buffalo Fire Historical Society
1850 William Street
Buffalo, NY 14206
(716) 892-8400

Capen Hope Co. No. 4 - Fire Museum
237 South Main Street
Brockport, NY 14716
(716) 637-4713

Centerport Fire Museum
Centerport, NY

Clinton Fire Department Museum
Clinton Fire Department
Clinton NY

Dobbs Ferry Fire Museum
Lt. John Cullen
489 Benedict Avenue
Tarrytown, NY 10591
(914) 631-8511

Fire Services Academy Museum
50 Lincoln Boulevard
Bethpage, NY 11714
(516) 735-6499

Firemen's Memorial Exhibit Ctr. of Western NY
3359 Broadway
Cheektowago, NY 14227

Historic 1897 Firehouse - Old Fire Sta. 4
PO Box 103
Elmira, NY 14902-0103
(607) 734-6689
e-mail: station4@stny.rr.com

Homeville Antique Fire Department
32 Center Street
Homer, New York 13077
(607) 749-4466

Hooper Fire Museum
331 East Main Street
Endwell, NY 13760
(607) 785-2279

Islip Town Firefighters Museum
P.O. Box 674
Sayville, NY 11782

The John D. Murray Firefighter's Museum
Box 211
Oswego, NY 13126
(315) 343-0999

Middle Island Fire Department
53 Swezeytown Road
Middle Island, NY 11953

New York City Fire Museum
278 Spring Street
New York, NY 10013
(212) 691-1303

Orange County Firefighters Museum
P. O. Box 388
Montgomery, NY 12549

Troy Fire Department Museum
RD 1, West Sandlake Road
Rensselar, NY 12144
(518) 272-9721

Vol. Firemen's Hall & Museum of Kingston
265 Fair Street
C. P. O. Box 1501
Kingston, NY 12401
(914) 331-0866

Ye Old Fire Station Museum
8662 Cicero-Brewerton Road
Cicero, NY 13039
(315) 699-3642 or 699-2761

Ohio

Central Fire Museum
800 South Washington Street
Van Wert, OH 45891
(419) 238-1010

Central Ohio Fire Museum & Learning Ctr.
260 North Fourth Street
Columbus, OH 43215
(419) 464-4099

Cincinnati Fire Museum
315 West Court Street
Cincinnati, OH 45202
(513) 621-5571

Firefighter's Museum Inc.
111 West First Street - Suite 718
Dayton, OH 45402-9869

Honey Creek Fire Museum
315 North Adams Street
New Carlisle, OH 45344
(937) 845-0480

Lima Fire Museum
Lima, OH 44906

Mansfield Fire Museum
1265 W Fourth Street
Mansfield, OH 44906
(419) 529-2573

Toledo Firefighters Museum
918 Sylvania
Toledo, OH 43612
(419) 478-3473

Varnes' Fire Museum
8168 South Bedford Road
Macedonia, OH 44056
(216) 467-8783

Western Reserve Fire Museum
P.O. Box 93463
Cleveland, OH 44101

Oklahoma

Oklahoma State Firefighters Museum
2716 NE 50th Street
Oklahoma City, OK 73111
(405) 424-1452

Oregon

Oregon Fire Service Museum and Learning Center
4762 Portland Road, N.E.
Salem, OR 97305
(503) 390-8253 ext. 204

Portland Fire Bureau Museum
55 S.W. Ash Street
Portland, OR 97204
(503) 823-3803

Uppertown Firefighters Museum
1618 Exchange Street
Astoria, OR 97103
(503) 325-2203

Pennsylvania

Beaver Creek Historic Fire Company
P.O. Box 358, RD 7
Coatsville, PA 19320
(215) 384-8962

Bethlehem Fire Dept. Memorial Fire Station
521 W. Broad St.
Bethlehem, PA 18018
(610) 865-7196

Chambersburg Vol. Fireman's Museum
441 Broad Street
Chambersburg, PA 17201
(717) 263-6215

Derry Fire Museum
Second Avenue, Route 116E
Derry, PA 15627
(412) 694-2653

Fire Fighters Historical Museum Inc.
428 Chestnut Street
Erie, PA 16507-1224
(814) 456-5969

Fire Museum of Greater Harrisburg
1820 North Fourth Street
Harrisburg, PA 17102
(717) 232-8915

Fire Museum of York County
757 West Market Street
York, PA 17404
(717) 843-0464

Fireman's Hall, Philadelphia, PA
147 North Second Street
Philadelphia, PA 19106
(215) 923-1438

Gibson Road Antique Fire Association
1545 Gibson Road
Bensalem, PA 19020
(215) 245-1545

Greensburg Fire Museum
416 South Main St.
P.O. Box 924
Greensburg, PA 15601
(412) 837-5355

Hanover Fire Museum
201 North Franklin Street
Hanover, PA 17331
(717) 637-6674

The Honesdale Fire Museum
Main and Park Streets
Honesdale, PA 18431

Schuylkill Historical Fire Society
105 South Jardin Street
Shenandoah, PA 17976
(570) 628-3691

Susquehanna Fire Department Museum
410 Elm Street
Susquehanna, PA 18847
(717) 853-4222

Union Fire Company No. 1 Museum
35 West Louther Street
Carlisle, PA 17013
(717) 243-2123

Rhode Island

Fireman's Museum
42 Baker Street
Warren, RI 02885
(401) 245-7600

Greenwood Vol. Fire Co. No 1 Museum
245 Morse Avenue
Warwick, RI 02886
(410) 737-6854

Jamestown Fire Museum
Narragansett Avenue
Jamestown, RI 02835
(401) 423-0062

South Carolina

Charleston Fire Department Museum
262 Meeting Place
Charleston, SC 29401

Columbia Fire Museum
Columbia Fire Department
Columbia, SC

Fire Station No. 1 Museum
400 South McDuffie
Anderson, SC 29624

Tennessee

Fire Museum of Memphis
118 Adams
Memphis, TN 38111
Ph: (901) 320-5650
fax: (901) 592-8422

Texas

Dallas Firefighters Museum
3801 Parry Avenue
Dallas, TX 75226
(214) 821-1500

Fire Museum of Texas
400 Walnut Street
P.O. Box 3827
Beaumont, TX 77704
(409) 880-3927

Houston Fire Museum
2403 Milam Street
Houston, TX 77006
(713) 524-2526

Nacogdoches Fire Museum
P.O. Drawer 630648
202 S. Fredonia
Nacogdoches, TX 75963-0648
(936) 559-2541

Texas Fire Museum
2600 Chalk Hill Rd.
Dallas, TX 75212-4506

Utah

Tremonton Firefighters Museum
102 South Tremont Street
Tremonton, UT 84337
435-257-3324

Virgina and Washington, DC

Friendship Fire Association Museum
4930 Connecticut Avenue NW
Washington, D.C. 20008
(301) 649-1321
(301) 649-1069 fax

Friendship Firehouse Museum
107 South Alfred Street
P. O. Box 22505
Alexandria, VA 22304
(703) 751-6416

Hopewell Fire Department
Hopewell, VA

James E. Lesnick Fire Museum
8804 Weir Street
Manassas, VA 22110
(703) 369-5869

Manassas Vol. Fire Co. and Fire Museum
Manassas Vol. Fire Co
Manassas, VA

Virginia Fire and Police Museum
200 West Marshall St.
Richmond, Va. 23220
(804) 644-1849

Vermont

Northfield Fire Department Museum
51 S, Main Street
Northfield, VT, 05663
(802) 485-6121
e-mail: wlyon@tds.net

Washington

Everett Firefighter's Hall & Fire Museum
2811 Oakes
Everett, WA 98201
(206) 259-8639 assoc.

Last Resort Fire Department
1433 N.W. 51st Street
Seattle, WA 98109
(206) 783-4474

Spokane Fire Station Museum
2511 North Lee St.
Spokane, WA 99207
509-625-7062

Vancouver Fire Department Museum
900 W. Evergreen Blvd.
Vancouver, WA 98660
(360) 696-8166

Wisconsin

Firehouse No. 3 Museum
700 Sixth Street
P.O. Box 081042
Racine, WI 53403
(414) 637-7395

Milwaukee Fire Historical Society
6680 N. Teutonia Ave
P.O. Box 412
Milwaukee, WI 53201

Old Fire Station No. 8 Museum
407 North Street
Madison, WI 53704
(608) 244-6732

Old Firehouse and Police Museum
Highway I-53, 23 Avenue East
P.O. Box 775
Superior, WI 54880
(715) 398-7558[

Preshtigo Fire Museum
400 Oconto Avenue
Preshtigo, WI 54057
(715) 582-3244

Venerable Fire Collection Inc.
4349 Hillside Rd.
Slinger, WI 53086
(262) 644-5784

CANADA

Canadian Fire Fighters Museum
P.O. Box 325
95 Mill Street South
Port Hope, ON L1A 3W4
(905) 885-8985

Canadian Fire Museum & Discovery Centre
P.O. Box 3520
Vermilion, AB T9X 2B5

Fire Fighter's Historical Soc. of Winnipeg Inc.
6 Mandan Road
Winnipeg, MB R2P 0V3

Firefighters Museum of Nova Scotia
451 Main Street
Yarmouth, NS B5A 1G9
(902) 742-5525

Firefighter's Museum Society - Calgary
4124-11 Street, S.E.
Calgary, Alberta T2G-3H2
(403) 252-0518

Halifax Fire Museum
Halifax Fire Department
Halifax, Nova Scotia.

Montreal Firefighters' Museum
5100 St-Laurent Blvd. (at Laurier St.)
Montreal, Quebec, Canada H2T 1R8
(514) 872-3757

Musee Bytown Fire Brigade Museum
1-2880 Shefield Road
Ottawa, ON K1B 1A4
(613) 744-0595

North York Fire Museum/Education Ctr.
59 Curfew Drive
North York, ON M3A 2P8
(416) 395-7228

Prince Rupert Fire Department Museum
200 West First Avenue
Prince Rupert, BC

Rossland Firehall Museum
Rossland, BC

Scarborough Fire Museum
35 Marilake Drive
Scarborough, ON M1S 1V8
(416) 297-8470

Victoria Fire Department Historical Society
1234 Yates Street
Victoria, BC V8V 3W8
(250) 920-3350
e-mail: DavidC._Noren@Telus.net

AUSTRALIA AND NEW ZEALAND

Adelaide Fire Museum
c/o S.A. Metropolitan Fire Service HQ
Wakefield Street
Adelaide,
Australia

Dannevirke Volunteer Fire Brigade Museum
P O Box 111
Dannevirke 5491
New Zealand
+64-6-374 7769

Fire Brigade Historical Society
39 Weenga Street
Geebung, Queensland, 43034,
Australia

Fire Museum & Educational Centre
Old Fire Station Headquarters
Hay St.
Perth, CBD
Australia

Jubilee Fire Museum
2 Chapel Street
(adjacent to Fire Station)
Masterton - Wairarapa Region
Ph: 378-6268, 377-1352

New Zealand Fire Service
93 Oreil Avenue
Westharbour, Auckland 8
New Zealand

S.A. Museum of Firefighting
Adelaide, South Australia
Currently under development,
but no permanent site yet
Enquiries to: The Secretary,
SAMF, PO Box 105,
Christie's Beach. S.A. 5165
Australia

Below: The Dalmatian, symbol of fire departments of a bygone era, poses atop a fire engine.

BIBLIOGRAPHY

Baum, Fred. "Ecclesiastical Architecture of California." *American Architect*, 34, July 1928).

Gebhard, David, and Robert Winter. *Los Angeles: An Architectural Guide.* Salt Lake City: Gibbs-Smith Publishers, 1994.

Halberstadt, Hans. *The American Fire Engine.* Osceola, Wisc.: Motorbooks International, 1993.

"The Hook & Letter" (newsletter), Summer 1994.

Los Angeles Examiner, July 21, 1954; July 22, 1954; June 10, 1955; July 13, 1955; October 28, 1955; November 18, 1955.

Los Angeles Herald & Express, February 2, 1956.

Maurath, Joe. "History of the Boston Fire Alarm Telegraph System." Yankee Pole Cat Insulator Club newsletter, August 1997.

O'Brien, John Joseph. "A History and Discussion of the Fire Alarm System of San Francisco" (report to the San Francisco Fire Department), April 2, 1951.

"The Toldeo Fire and Police Alarm Telegraph Systems" (staff report), February 10, 1937.

Toledo Fire Division. "The Mighty Seed, The Fire Horse" (report), vol. 2, 1837–1983.

Wagner, Rob Leicester. *Fire Engines.* New York: MetroBooks, 1996.

Zurier, Rebecca. *The American Firehouse: An Architectural and Social History.* New York: Abbeville Press, 1982.

PHOTO CREDITS

©Adam Alberti: 77, *84-85*

Aurora: ©Jose Azel: *103*

City of Alexandria, VA: ©Anna Frame: *10*

©Ed Cooper Photo: *12, 58-59, 59, 65, 107*

Corbis: *18, 19, 32, 33, 39, 44, 89 top;* ©James L. Amos: *98 top;* ©Bettmann: *30, 45 top;* ©Lowell Georgia: *56 both;* ©Charles Harris/ Pittsburgh Courier: *89 bottom;* ©Hulton-Deutsch Collection: *45 bottom;* ©Michael Maslan Historic Photographs: *36 bottom;* ©Minnesota Historical Society: *23, 46 top, 47;* ©Jack Moebes: *88;* ©Museum of History & Industry: *34, 64;* ©Museum of The City of New York: *24, 106;* ©Arthur Rothstein: *68;* ©Joseph Schwartz Collection: *54 bottom;* ©Lee Snider: *20, 104;* ©Ted Streshinsky: *98 bottom, 100 bottom;* ©Adam Woolfitt: *14*

©Richard Cummins: *27, 105*

Dembinsky Photo Assoc.: ©Dan Dempster: *74-75, 78-79;* ©Bob Freeman: *73;* ©Joseph Pinto: *2, 36 top, 82;* ©Jim Regan: *48*

©Charlene Faris: *56*

FPG: *22, 28-29, 31, 35, 55, 80;* ©Richard Stockton: *42-43;* ©Jeffrey Sylvester: *112*

©John K. Gates: *60*

H. Armstrong Roberts: *6-7;* ©J. McGrail: *16-17*

Courtesy of the Houston Fire Museum: *70-71*

The Image Finders: ©Eric R. Berndt: *76-77*

©Dick James: *15*

©Bruce Leighty: *6, 12, 49, 91*

David Lewis Collection: *38, 40-41, 42, 69, 95 top, 96-97, 99;* ©David Lewis: *100 top*

New England Stock Photo: ©Tony LaGruth: *26, 117;* ©Lou Palmieri: *86 top;* ©Jim Schwabel: *61*

©New Wave Photography: *21, 66, 100-101*

©Bill Noonan: *24-25, 50-51, 52-53, 54 top left & right, 62, 63, 67, 72, 81, 83, 94, 95 bottom, 102*

©Robert Perron: *86 bottom*

Place Stock Photo: ©Thomas I. Morse: *114-115*

Courtesy of the Sierra Madre Public Library: *8-9*

Stone: ©Gary Benson: *87*

©Superstock: *110*

©Kevin Ullrich: *46 bottom*

©Underwood Photo Archives, Inc.: *37, 108-109, 113*

©Steve Warble: *90*

©Petronella Ytsma: *92, 93*

Digital Retouching, Daniel J. Rutkowski: *46 bottom*

INDEX